Non-Verbal Reasoning

The 11+ Practice Book

with Assessment Tests

Ages

9-10

Practise • Prepare • Pass

Everything your child needs for 11+ success

How to use this Practice Book

This book is divided into two parts — Spotting Patterns and Assessment Tests.
There are answers and detailed explanations in the pull-out section at the back of the book.

Spotting Patterns

- Each section contains practice questions focusing on one of the main concepts your child will need to understand for the Non-Verbal Reasoning test.
- These pages can help your child build up the different skills they'll need for the real test.

Assessment Tests

- The second half of the book contains six assessment tests, each with a mix of question types. They're similar to the real test.
- You can print off multiple-choice answer sheets from our website, www.cgplearning.co.uk/11+, so your child can practise taking the tests as if they're sitting the real thing.
- If you want to give your child timed practice, set a time limit of 25 minutes for each test, and ask them to work as quickly and carefully as they can.
- The tests get harder from 1-6, so don't be surprised if your child finds the later ones more tricky.
- Talk your child through the answers to the questions they got wrong. This will help them understand questions that work in a similar way when they come up against them in later tests.
- Your child should aim for a mark of around 85% (39 questions correct) in each test. If they score less than this, use their results to work out the areas they need more practice on.
- If they haven't managed to finish the test on time, they need to work on increasing their speed, whereas if they have made a lot of mistakes, they need to work more carefully.
- Keep track of your child's scores using the progress chart on the inside back cover of the book.

Published by CGP

Editors:
David Broadbent, Ceara Hayden, Rebecca Tate and Luke von Kotze

With thanks to Claire Boulter and Amanda MacNaughton for the proofreading.

ISBN: 978 1 84762 834 3
Printed by Elanders Ltd, Newcastle upon Tyne
Clipart from Corel®

Based on the classic CGP style created by Richard Parsons.

Contents

Spotting Patterns

Assessment Tests

Shapes

When you see a question about shapes, counting their sides is often a good place to start.

Warm Up

1. How many **sides** does each of these shapes have?

a. b. 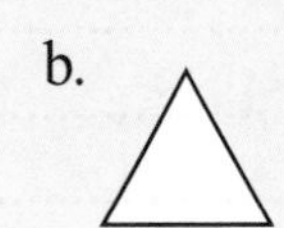 c. d. e. f. g.

____ ____ ____ ____ ____ ____ ____

2. How many **lines of symmetry** does each shape have?

a. b. 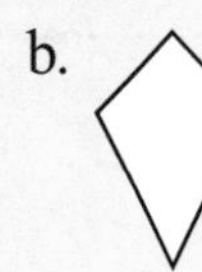 c. d. e. 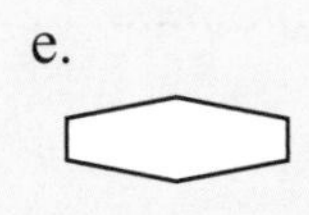 f. g. 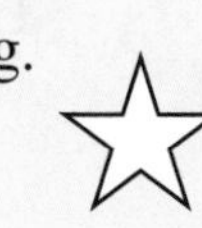

____ ____ ____ ____ ____ ____ ____

3. Find one thing that each set of shapes has **in common**.

a.   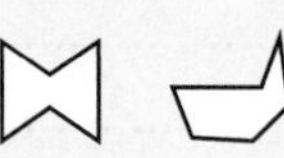 b. 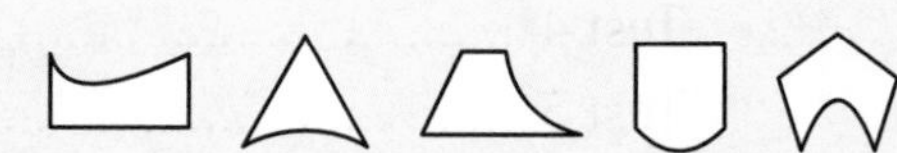

____________________ ____________________

Odd One Out

Look at the five figures below. Find which figure is most unlike the others.

Example:

 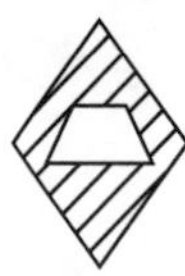   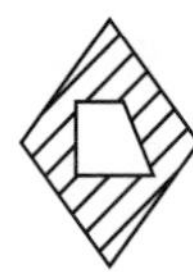

a b c d e (d)

All the other big diamonds have four-sided shapes inside them.

4.

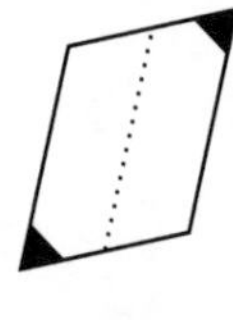    

a b c d e (____)

5.

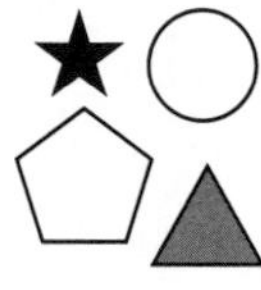 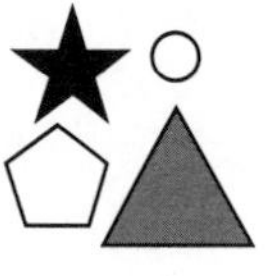 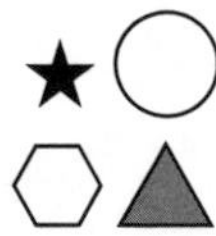 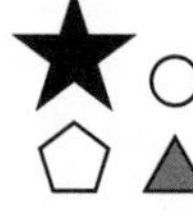 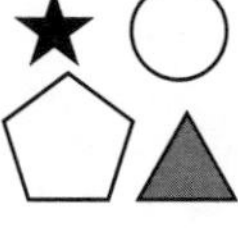

a b c d e (____)

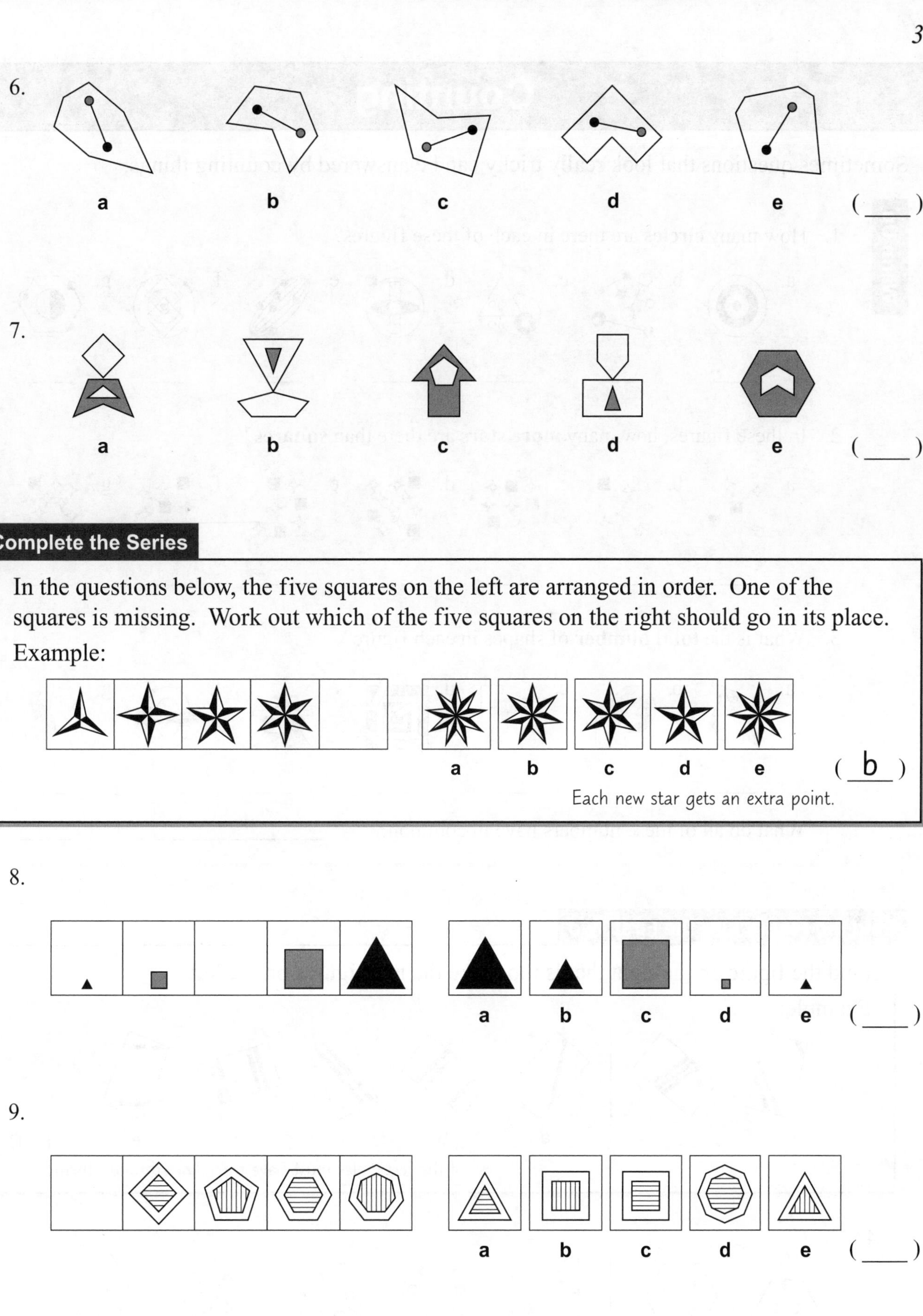

Complete the Series

In the questions below, the five squares on the left are arranged in order. One of the squares is missing. Work out which of the five squares on the right should go in its place.

Example:

10.

a b c d e (____)

Counting

Sometimes questions that look really tricky can be answered by counting things.

Warm Up

1. How many **circles** are there in each of these figures?

a.  b. 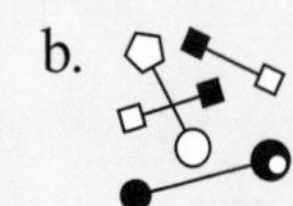 c.  d.  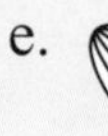 e. 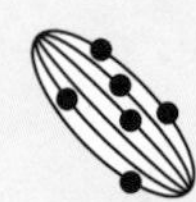  f. 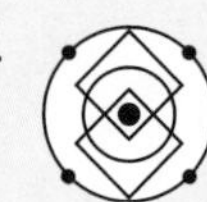  g. 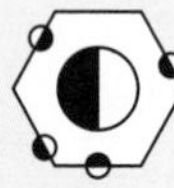

____ ____ ____ ____ ____ ____ ____

2. In these figures, how many **more stars** are there than **squares**?

a. 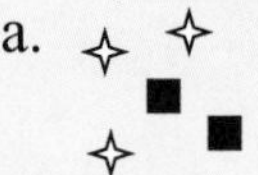 b.  c. 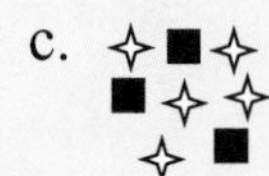 d.  e.  f. 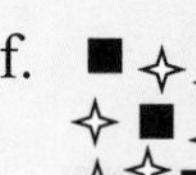  g. 

____ ____ ____ ____ ____ ____ ____

3. What is the **total number** of shapes in each figure?

a.  b. 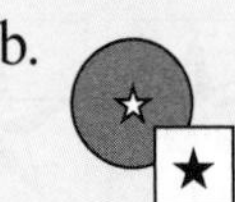 c. 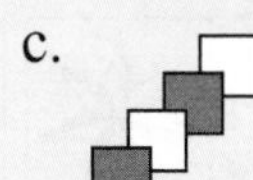 d.  e.  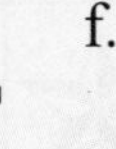 f. 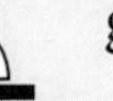 g. 

____ ____ ____ ____ ____ ____ ____

What do all of these numbers have in common? ________________

Find the Figure Like the First Two

Find the figure on the right that is most like the two figures on the left.

Example:

  | 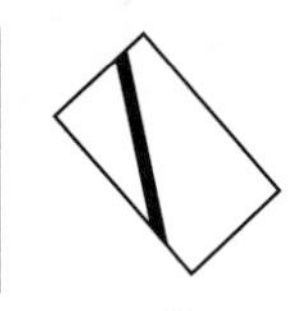    

a b c d e (b)

All of the rectangles must have three lines through them.

4. 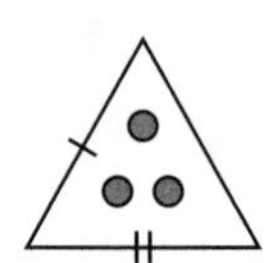 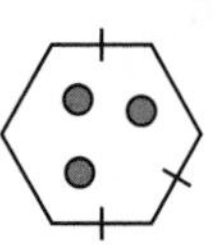 | 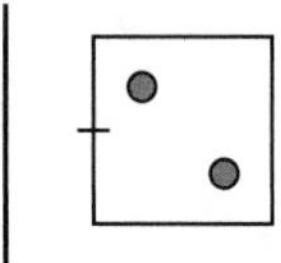 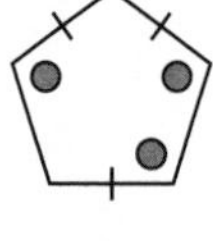 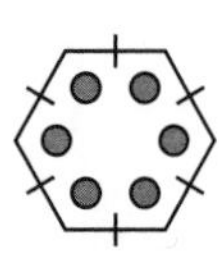 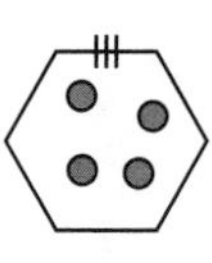 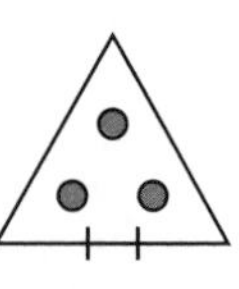

a b c d e (____)

5.  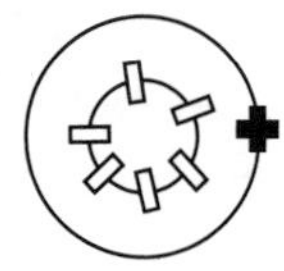 | 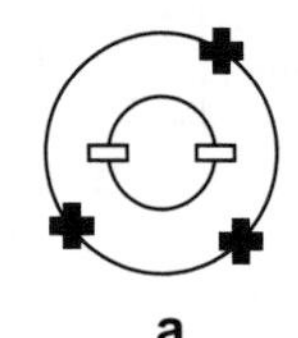 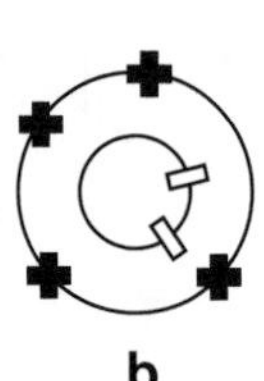 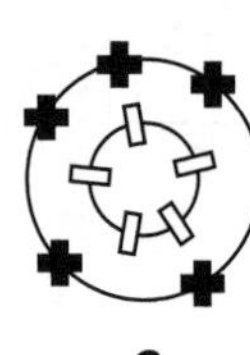 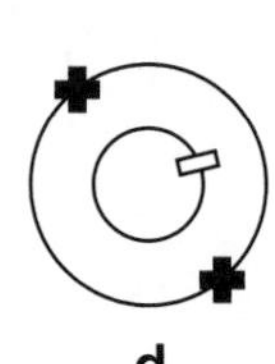 

a b c d e (____)

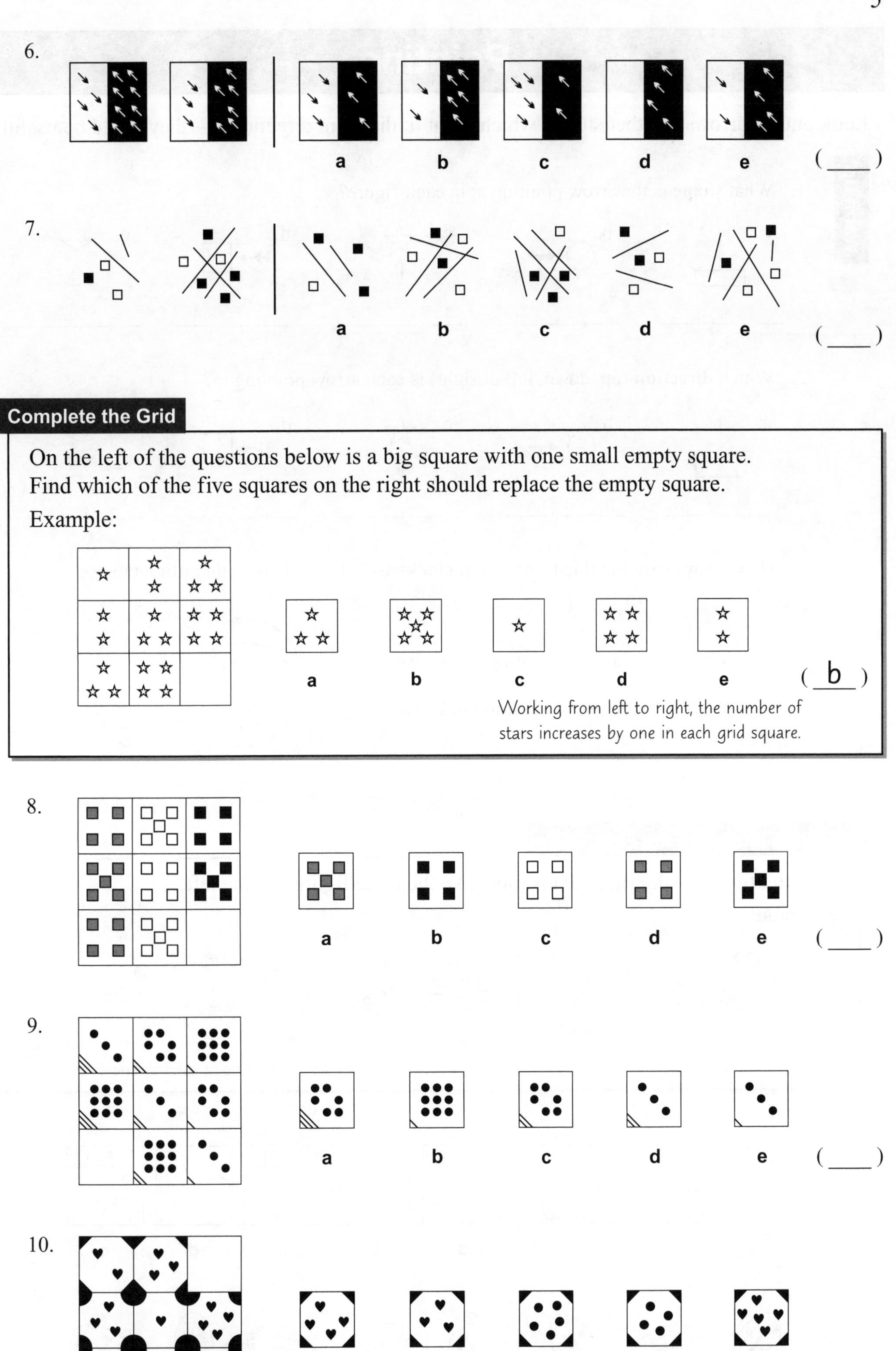
6.
a
b
c
d
e
(____)
7.
a
b
c
d
e
(____)
Complete the Grid
On the left of the questions below is a big square with one small empty square.
Find which of the five squares on the right should replace the empty square.
Example:
a
b
c
d
e
(b)
Working from left to right, the number of stars increases by one in each grid square.
8.
a
b
c
d
e
(____)
9.
a
b
c
d
e
(____)
10.
a
b
c
d
e
(____)

Pointing

Look out for arrows or other shapes which point in different directions — they could be useful.

Warm Up

1. What **shape** is the arrow pointing at in each figure?

a. 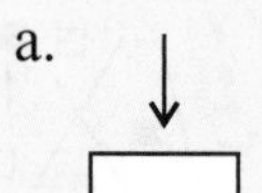 b. 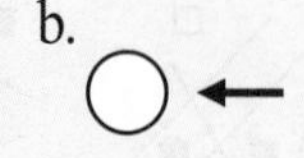 c. 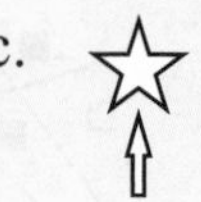 d. 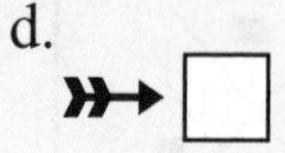 e. 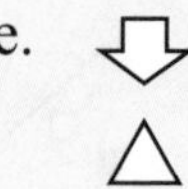

________ ________ ________ ________ ________

2. Which **direction** (up, down, left or right) is each arrow pointing in?

a. 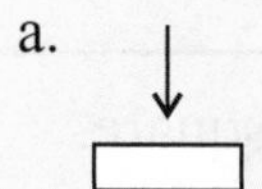 b. 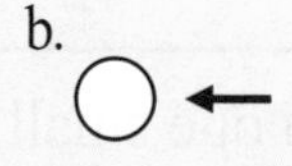 c. 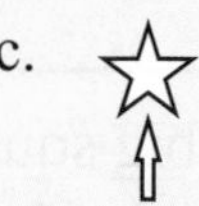 d.  e. 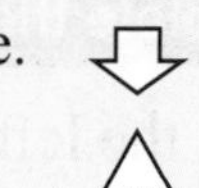

________ ________ ________ ________ ________

3. How many arrows in this figure point **clockwise**? How many point **anticlockwise**?

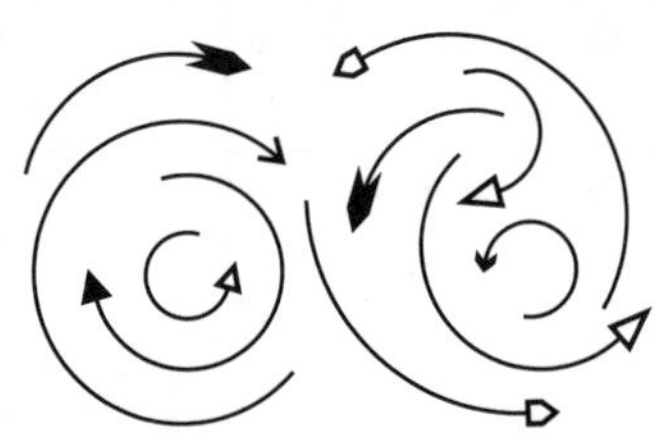

Number of arrows pointing **clockwise**: ____

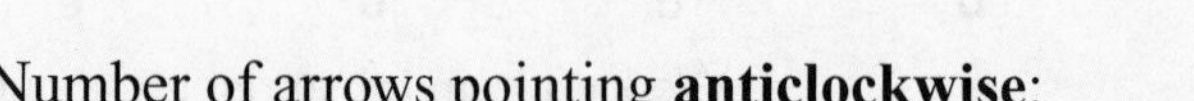

Number of arrows pointing **anticlockwise**: ____

Find the Figure Like the First Three

Find the figure on the right that is most like the three figures on the left.

Example:

  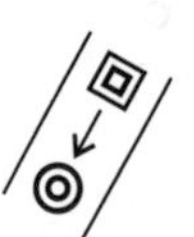 |  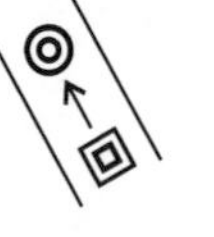 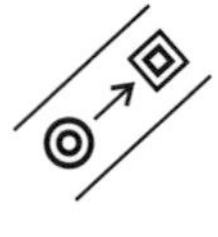 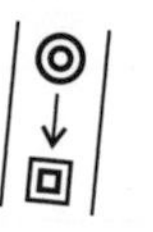 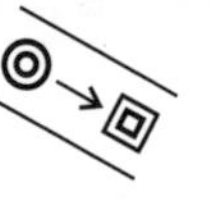

a b c d e (b)

The arrow must point towards the circle.

4. 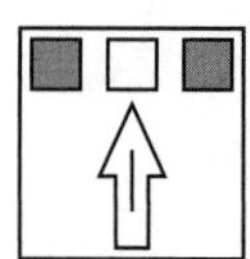 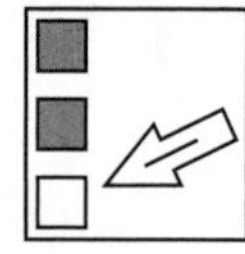 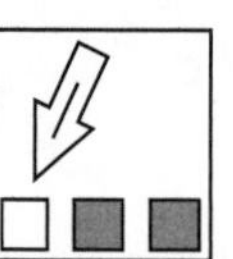 | 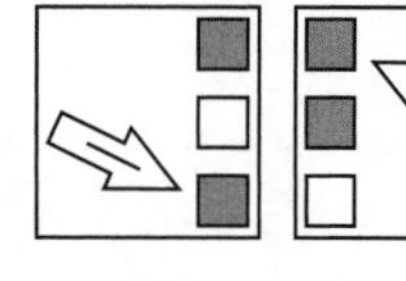  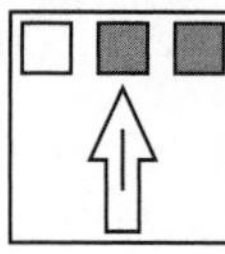 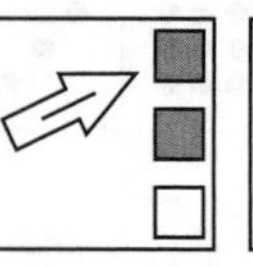 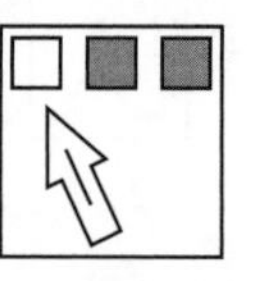

a b c d e (____)

5.  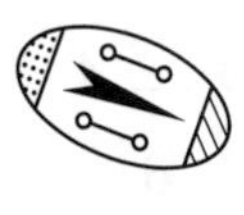  |  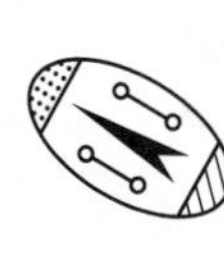 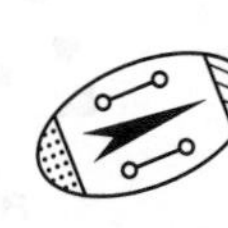 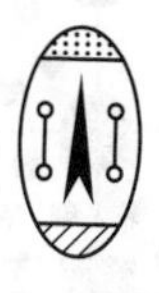 

a b c d e (____)

6.

7.

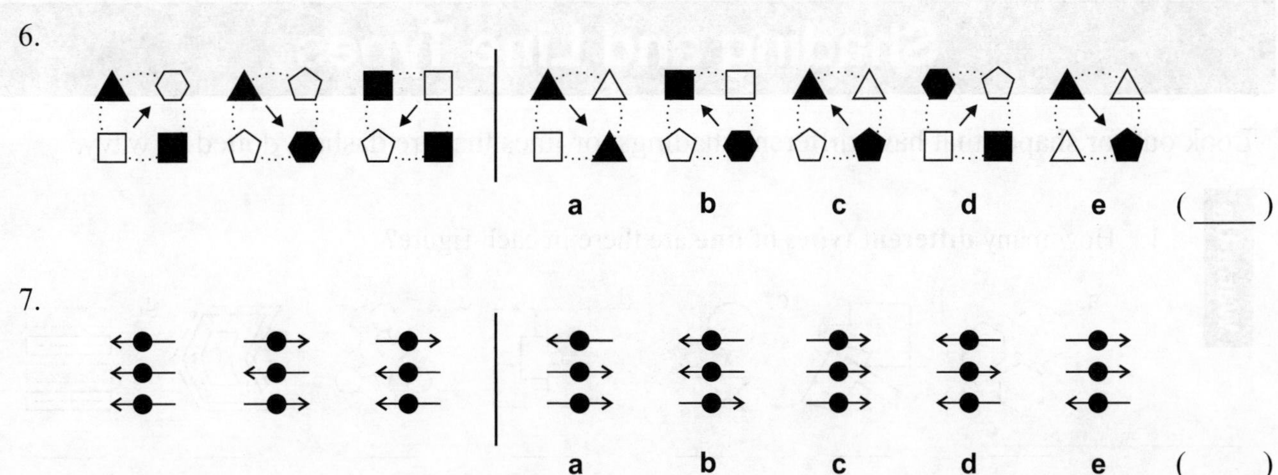

Horizontal Code

In the boxes on the left are shapes with code letters. The top letters have a different meaning from the bottom ones. Work out how the letters go with the shapes and then find the code for the new shape from the five codes on the right.

Example:

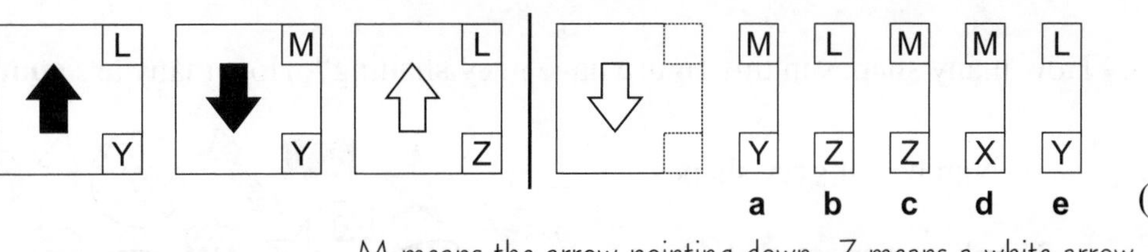

(C)

M means the arrow pointing down. Z means a white arrow.

8.

9.

10.

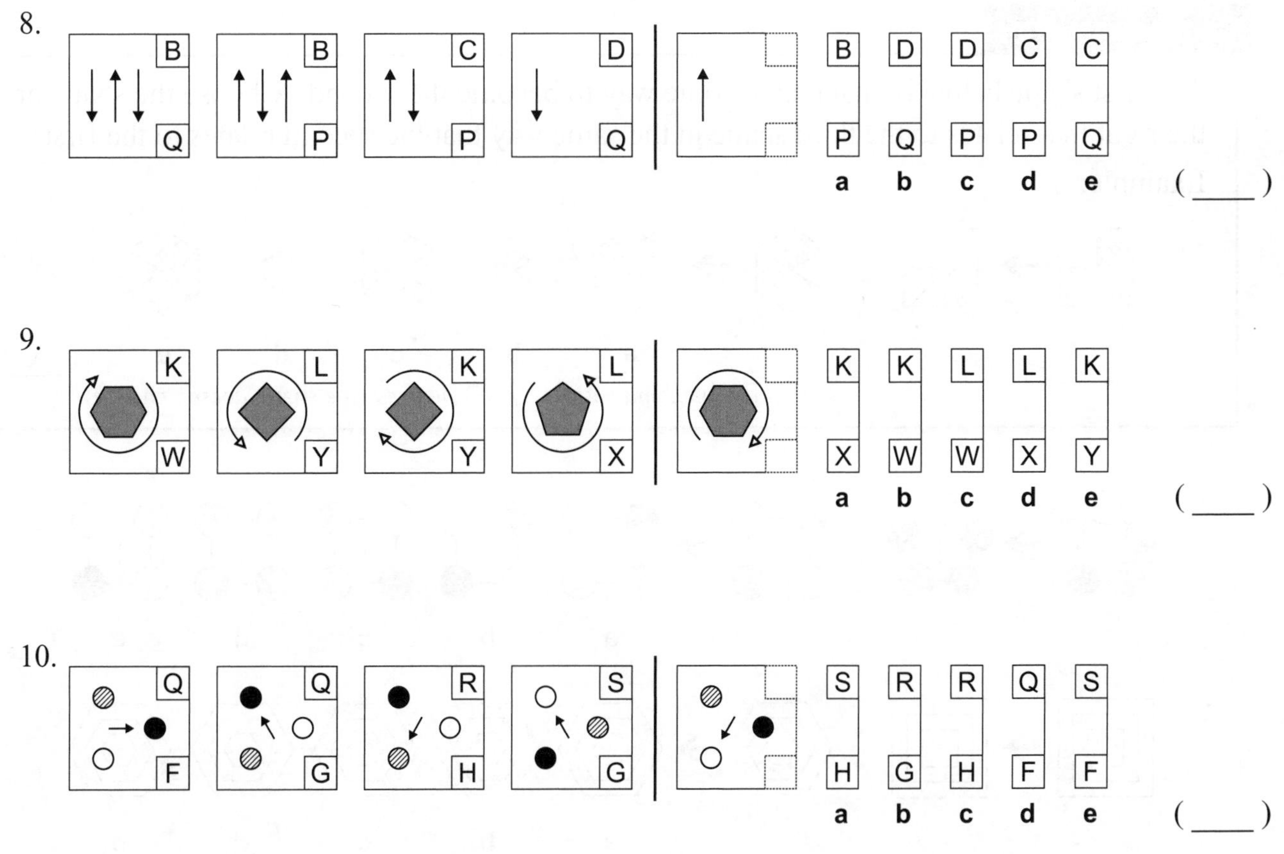

Shading and Line Types

Look out for shapes that have different shadings, or lines that are dashed, dotted or wavy.

Warm Up

1. How many **different types of line** are there in each figure?

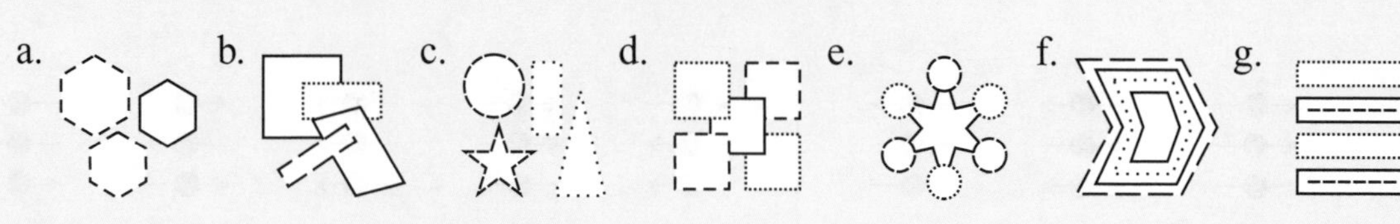

a. ____ b. ____ c. ____ d. ____ e. ____ f. ____ g. ____

2. Look at each shape (a to g) and write down the number of the **circle** with the **same shading**.

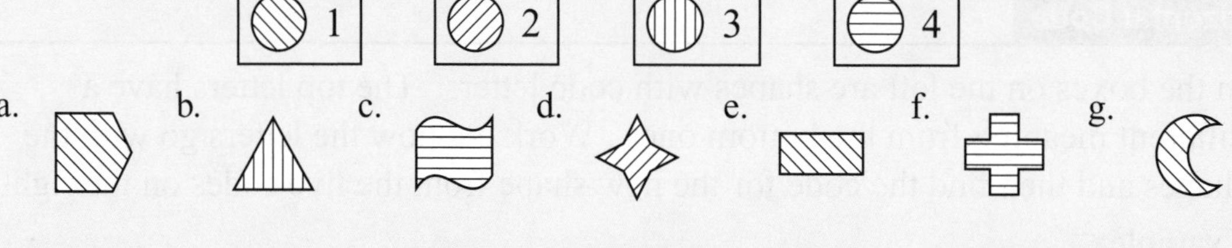

a. ____ b. ____ c. ____ d. ____ e. ____ f. ____ g. ____

3. How many shapes in this figure have **grey** shading? How many are **spotted**?

Number of **grey** shapes: ____

Number of **spotted** shapes: ____

Complete the Pair

The first shape below is changed in some way to become the second. Choose the shape on the right that relates to the third shape in the same way that the second relates to the first.

Example:

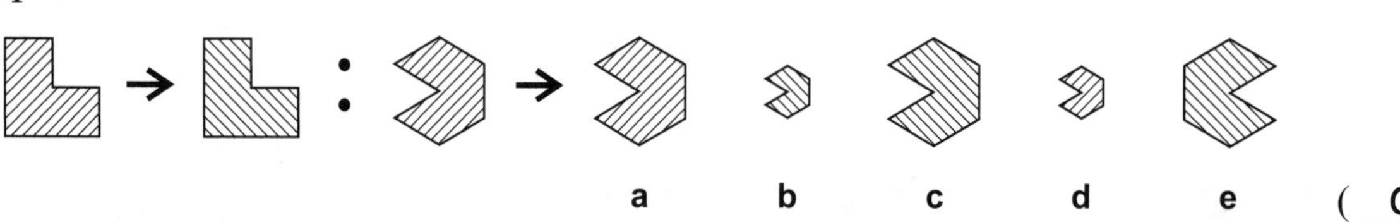

a b c d e (C)

The hatching rotates by 90 degrees (the shape doesn't change).

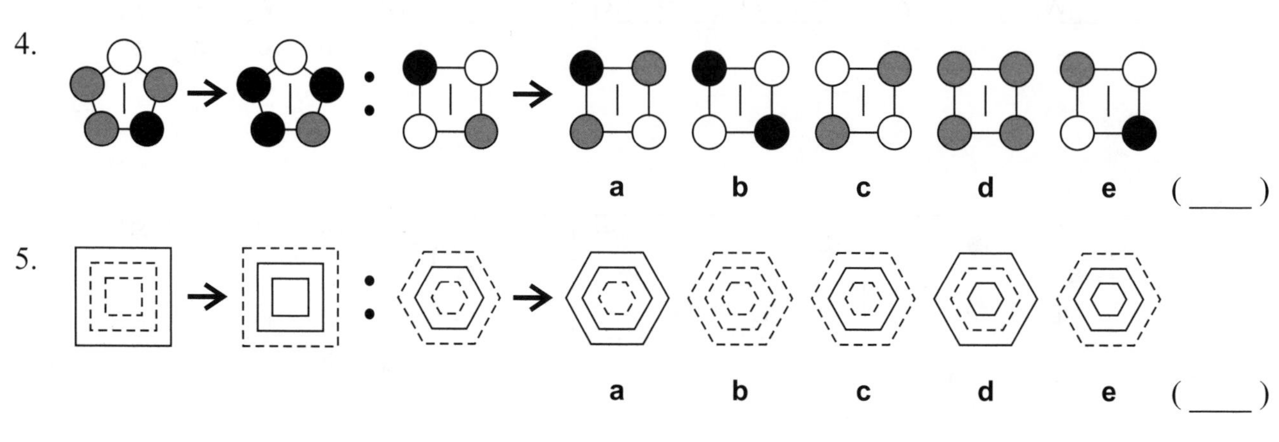

4. a b c d e (____)

5. a b c d e (____)

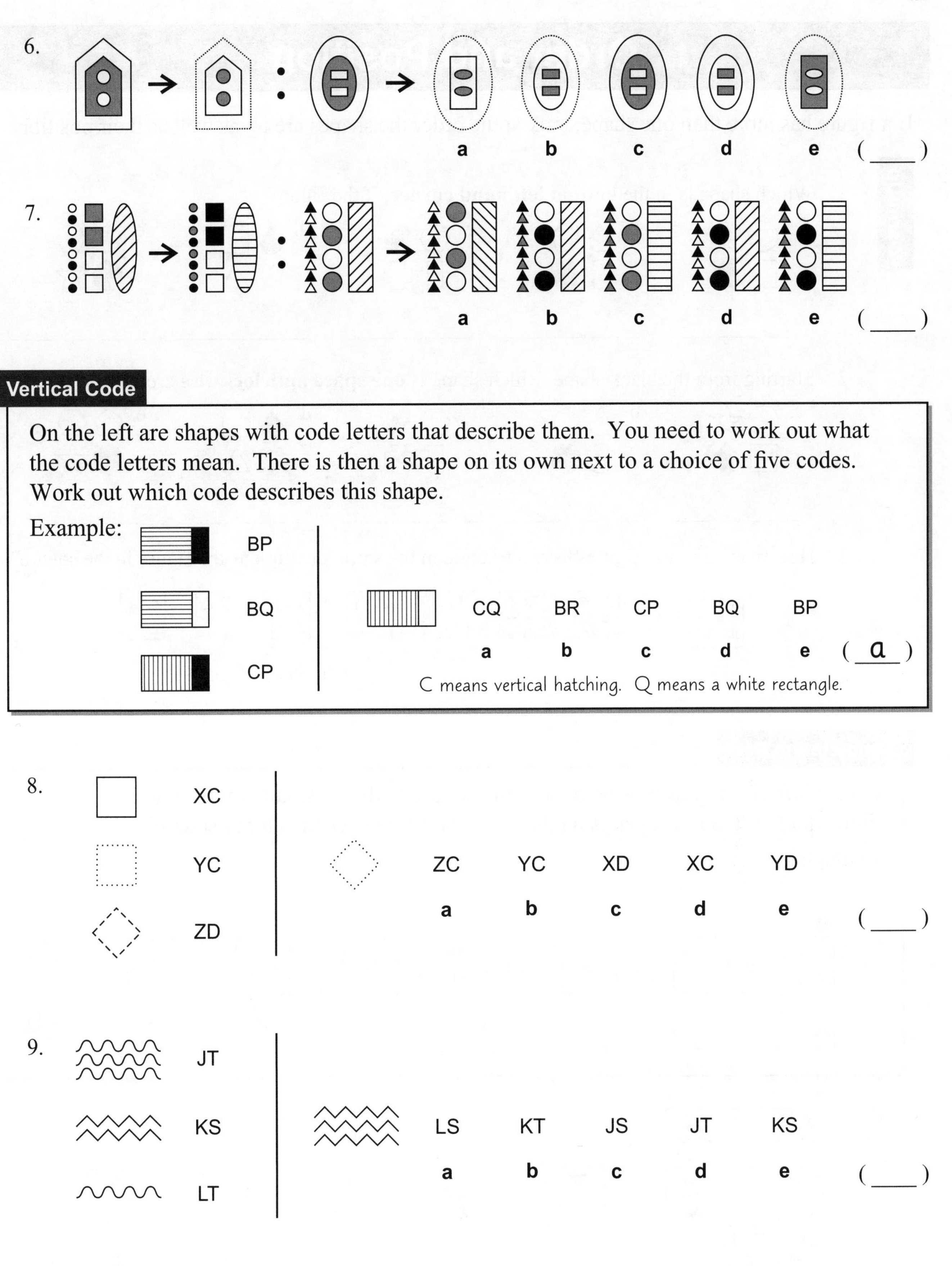

Vertical Code

On the left are shapes with code letters that describe them. You need to work out what the code letters mean. There is then a shape on its own next to a choice of five codes. Work out which code describes this shape.

Example:

10.

FV

HW

GX

HY

FW	HW	GX	FY	GY
a	b	c	d	e

(____)

Order and Position

If a figure has more than one shape, look at the order the shapes are in, as well as their positions.

Warm Up

1. Which shape is in the **bottom left hand corner** of the figure?

a.  b. 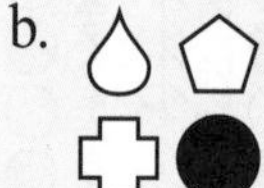 c.  d.  e. 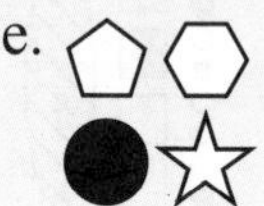

________ ________ ________ ________ ________

2. Starting from the black shape, which shape is **one space anticlockwise** around the figure?

a.  b. 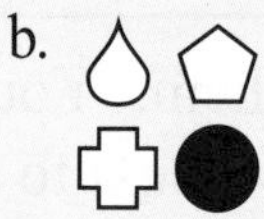 c. 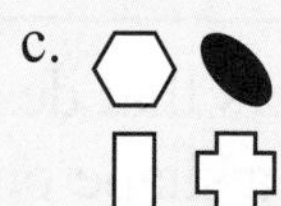 d.  e. 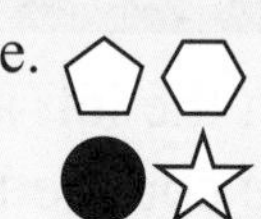

________ ________ ________ ________ ________

3. How many of these figures have a triangle in the **same position** as the figure in the square?

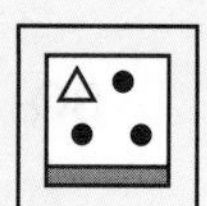 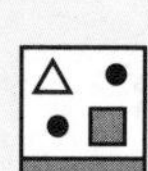      

Number of figures: ____

Complete the Grid

On the left of the questions below is a big square with one small empty square.
Find which of the five squares on the right should replace the empty square.

Example:

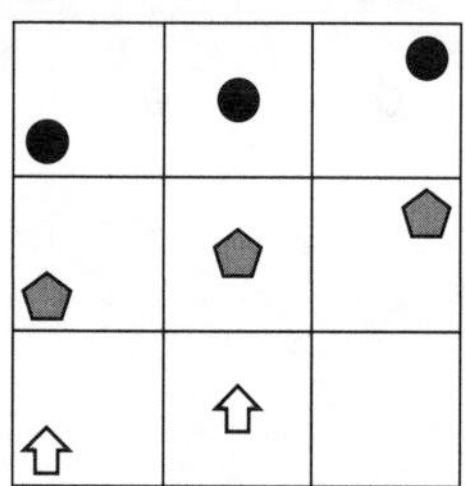

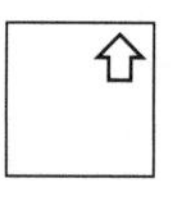 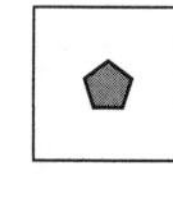 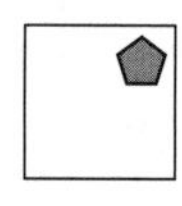 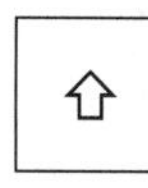

a b c d e (b)

Moving from left to right, the shape moves diagonally up to the right.

4. 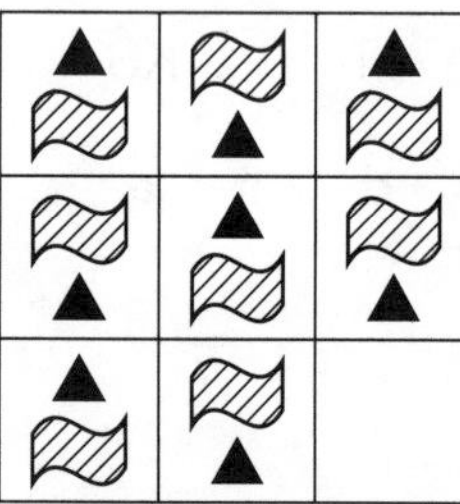

a b c d e (____)

5. 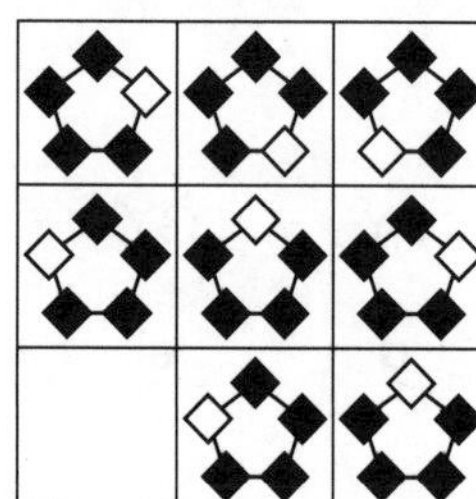

   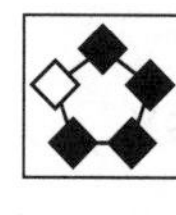 

a b c d e (____)

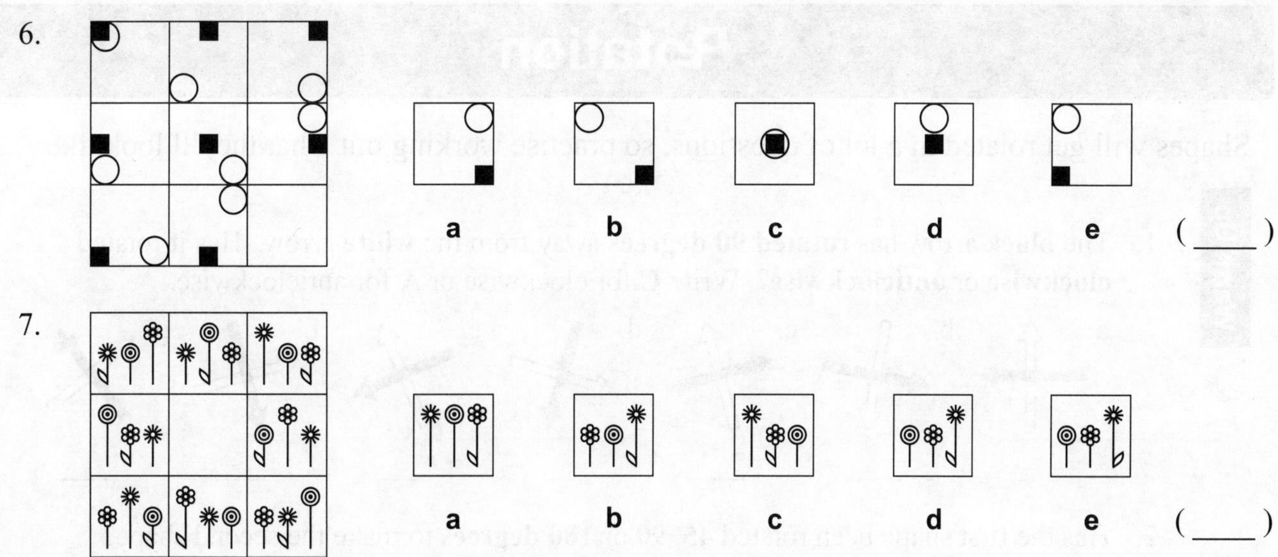

Find the Figure Like the First Three

Find the figure on the right that is most like the three figures on the left.

Example:

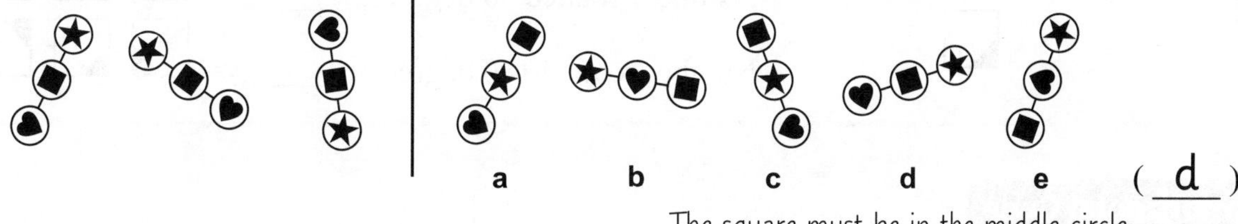

The square must be in the middle circle.

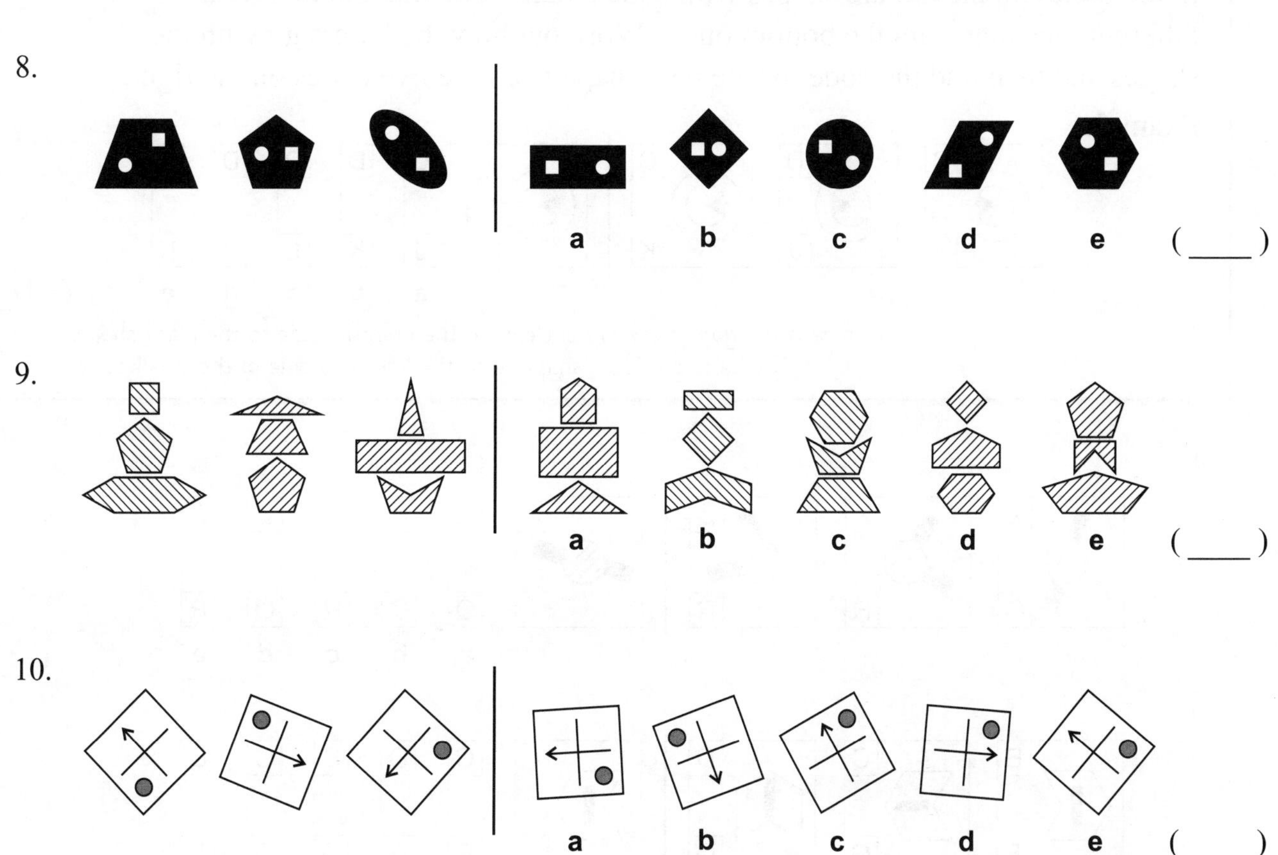

Rotation

Shapes will get rotated in a lot of questions, so practise working out what they'll look like.

Warm Up

1. The **black** arrow has **rotated 90 degrees** away from the **white** arrow. Has it rotated **clockwise** or **anticlockwise**? Write **C** for clockwise or **A** for anticlockwise.

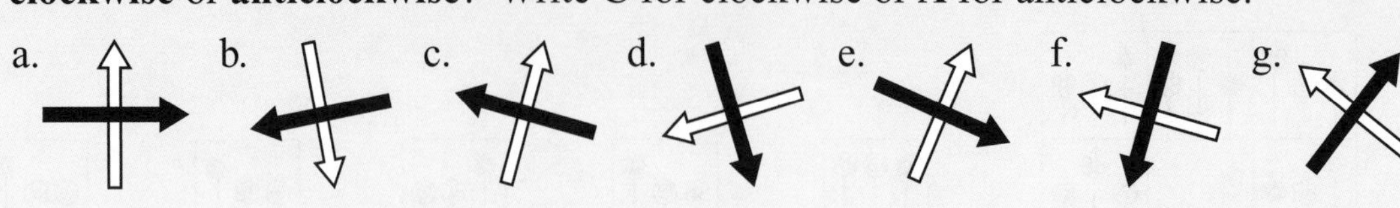

2. Has the first shape been rotated **45**, **90** or **180 degrees** to make the second shape?

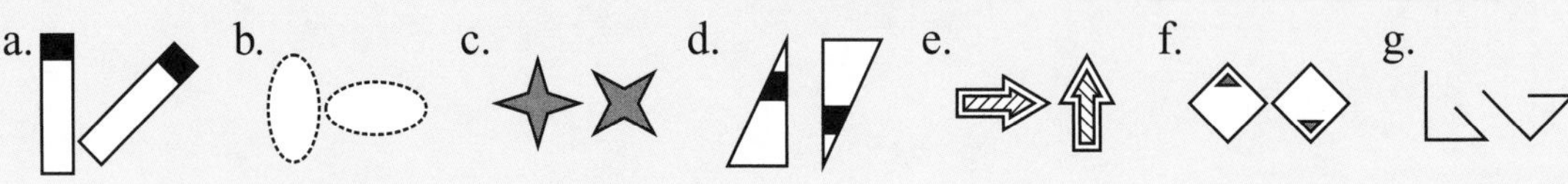

3. How many squares have been rotated **90 degrees** or **180 degrees** from the example square?

Example square:

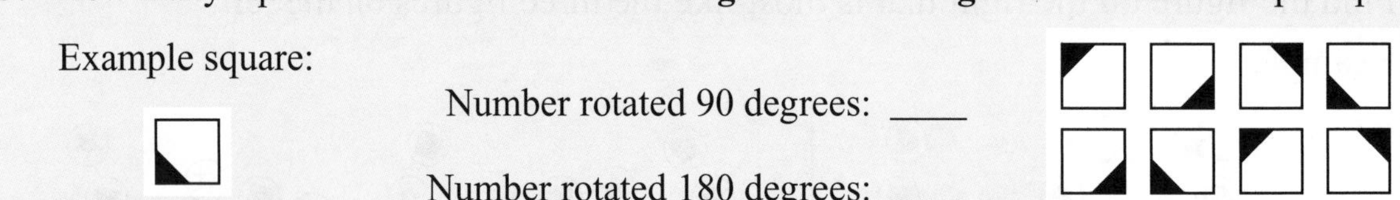

Number rotated 90 degrees: ____

Number rotated 180 degrees: ____

Horizontal Code

In the boxes on the left are shapes with code letters. The top letters have a different meaning from the bottom ones. Work out how the letters go with the shapes and then find the code for the new shape from the five codes on the right.

Example:

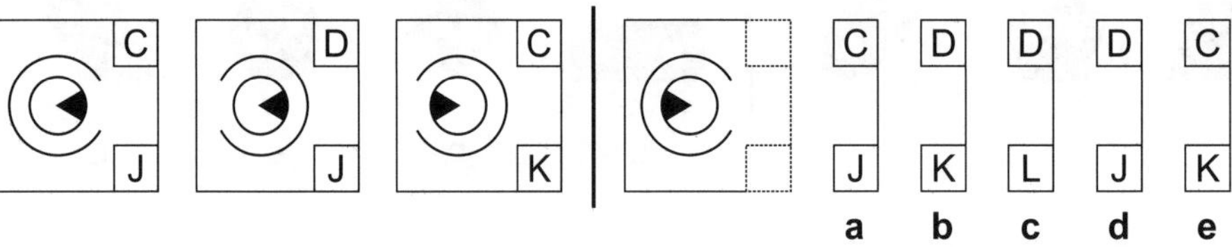

(b)

D means the gap in the big circle is on the opposite side to the black shape.
K means the black shape is on the left hand side of the small circle.

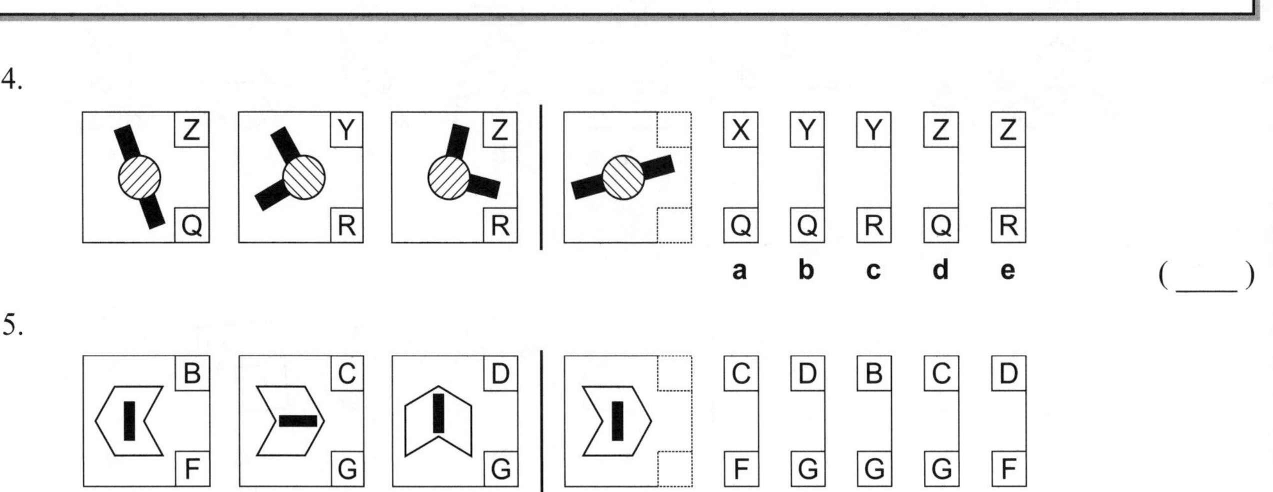

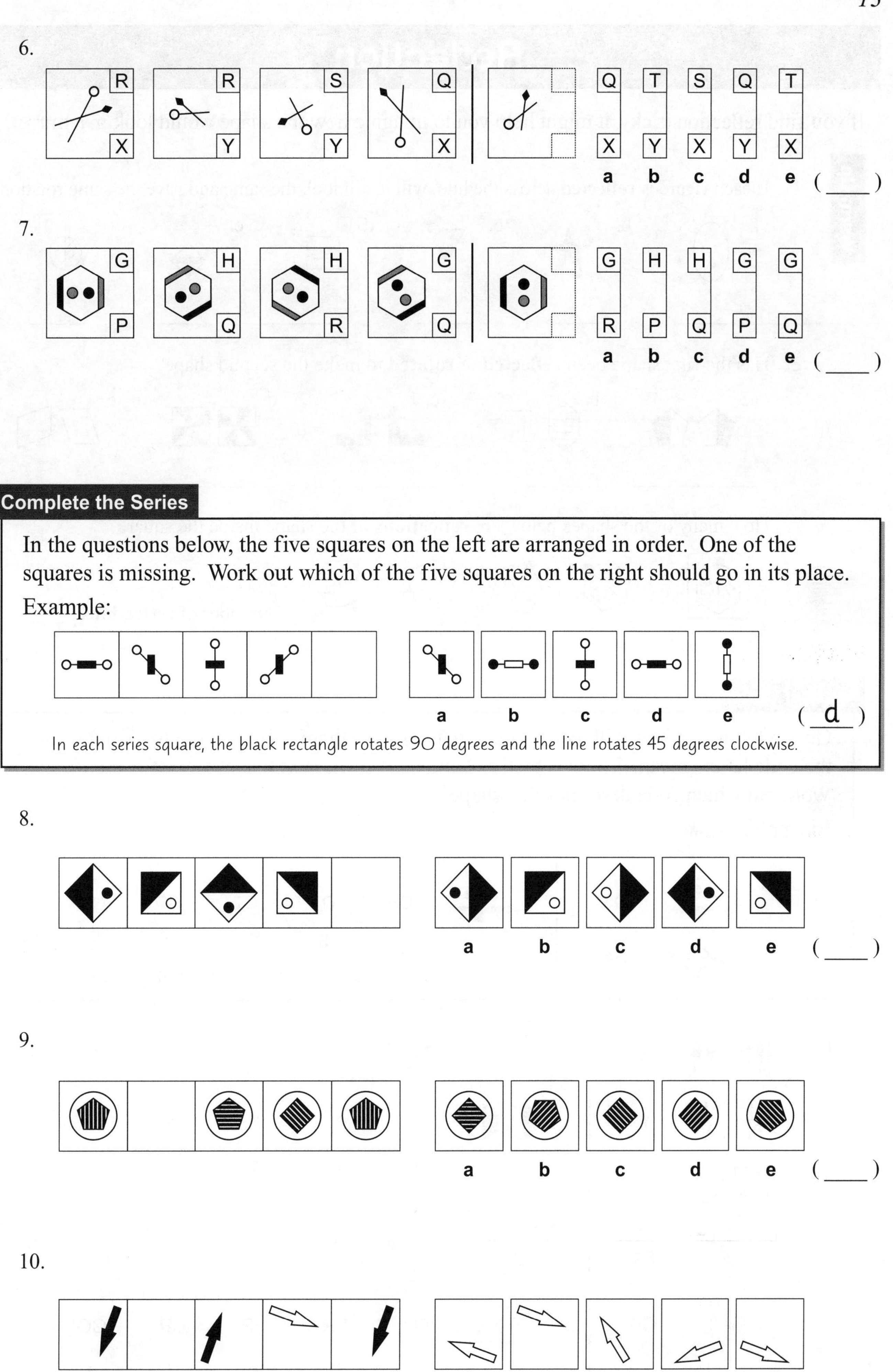

6.

a b c d e (___)

7.

a b c d e (___)

Complete the Series

In the questions below, the five squares on the left are arranged in order. One of the squares is missing. Work out which of the five squares on the right should go in its place.

Example:

a b c d e (d)

In each series square, the black rectangle rotates 90 degrees and the line rotates 45 degrees clockwise.

8.

a b c d e (___)

9.

a b c d e (___)

10.

a b c d e (___)

Reflection

If you find reflection tricky, it might help you to imagine how the shape would look in a mirror.

Warm Up

1. If each figure is **reflected** across the line, will it still look the same and have the same rotation?

a. 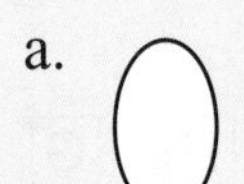 ____ b.  ____ c. 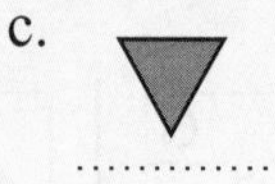 ____ d. 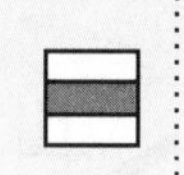 ____ e.  ____ f. 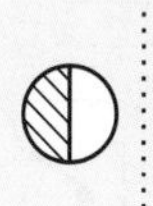 ____

2. Has the first shape been **reflected** or **rotated** to make the second shape?

a.  ____ b. 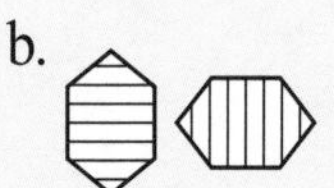 ____ c.  ____ d. 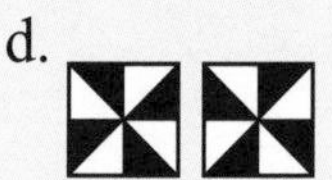 ____ e.  ____

3. How many of the shapes below are **reflections** of the shape inside the square?

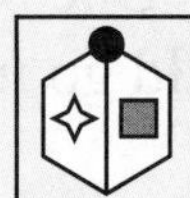    

Number of **reflections**: ____

Vertical Code

On the left are shapes with code letters that describe them. You need to work out what the code letters mean. There is then a shape on its own next to a choice of five codes. Work out which code describes this shape.

Example:

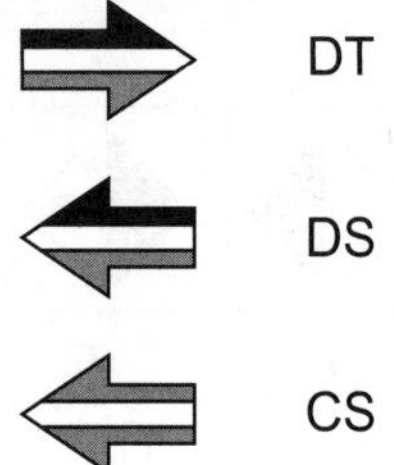

DS	DT	CT	BT	CS	
a	b	c	d	e	(C)

C means two grey stripes. T means the arrow points right.

4. 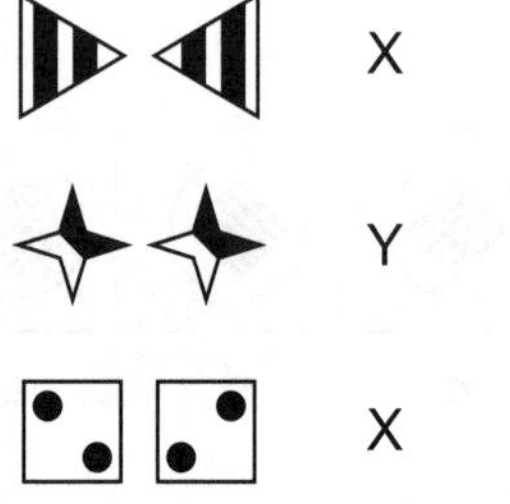

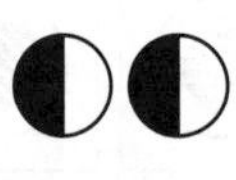

Z	Y	X	W	V	
a	b	c	d	e	(____)

5. 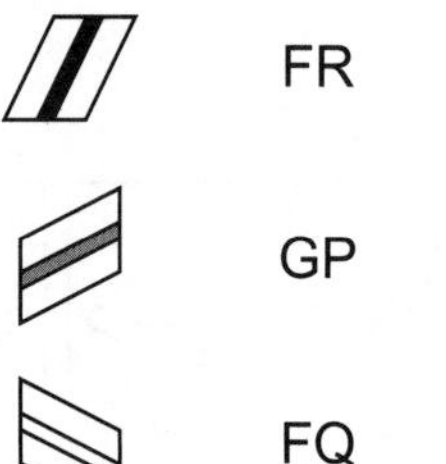

FQ	FR	FP	GR	GQ	
a	b	c	d	e	(____)

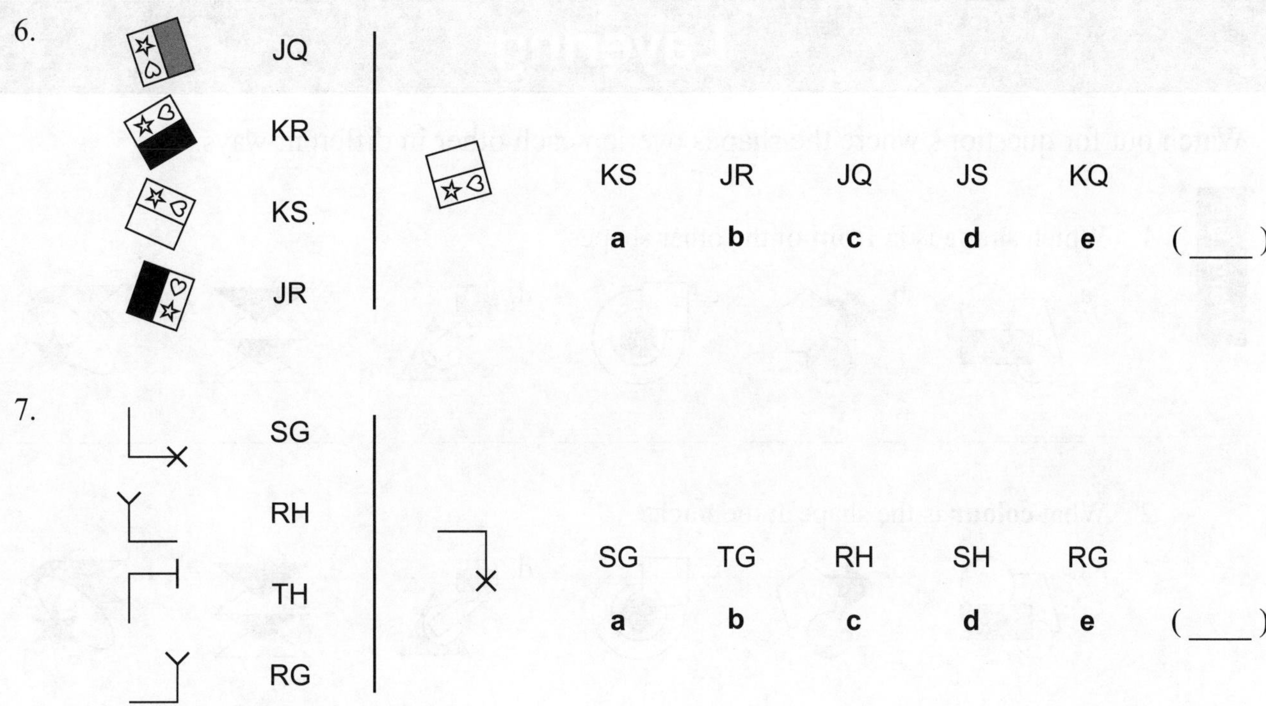

Find the Figure Like the First Two

Find the figure on the right that is most like the two figures on the left.

Example:

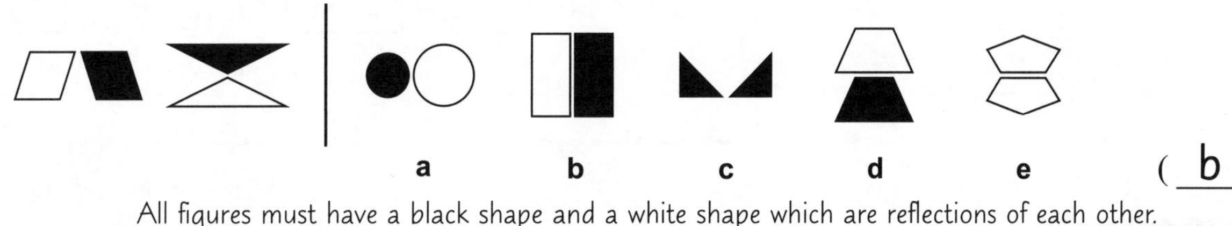

a b c d e (b)

All figures must have a black shape and a white shape which are reflections of each other.

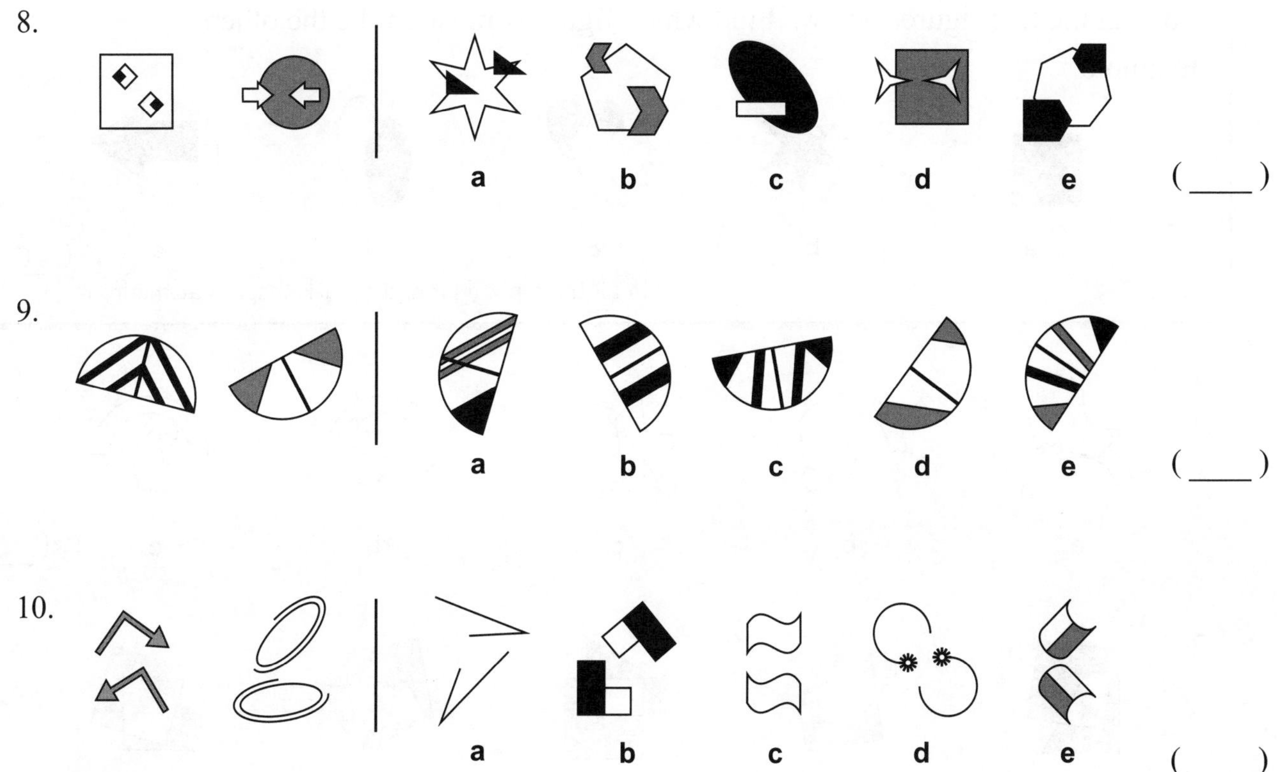

Layering

Watch out for questions where the shapes overlap each other in different ways.

Warm Up

1. Which **shape** is in **front** of the other shapes?

a. 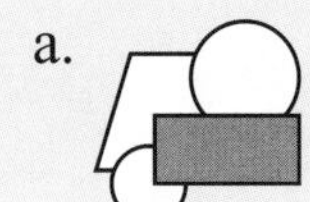 ________

b. 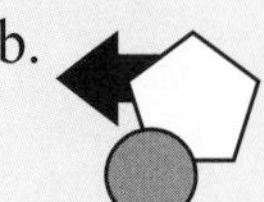 ________

c. 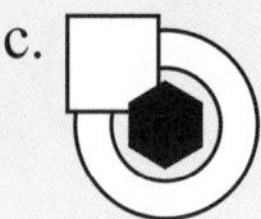 ________

d. 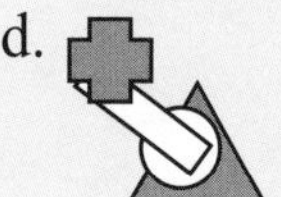 ________

e.  ________

f.  ________

2. What **colour** is the shape at the **back**?

a. 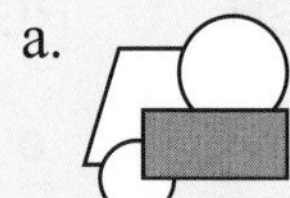 ________

b. ________

c. 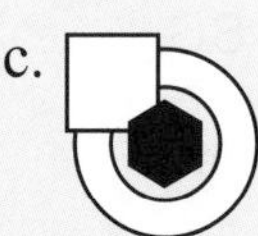 ________

d. 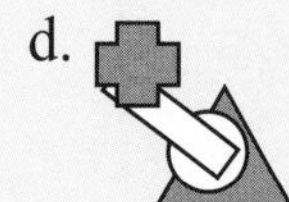 ________

e. ________

f.  ________

3. In the figures below, **extra shapes** have been made where the two shapes **overlap**. How many **sides** does each extra shape have?

a. 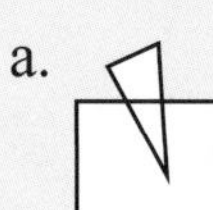 ____

b. ____

c. ____

d. 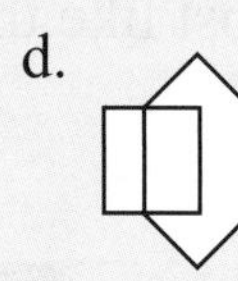 ____

e. 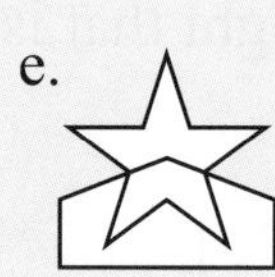 ____

f. 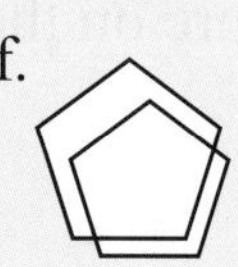 ____

g. ____

Odd One Out

Look at the five figures below. Find which figure is most unlike the others.

Example:

a

b

c

d

e

(C)

In all the other figures, the black shape is at the front.

4.

a

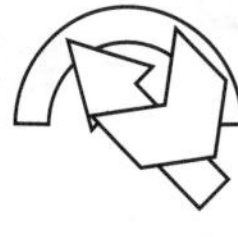
b

c

d

e

(____)

5.

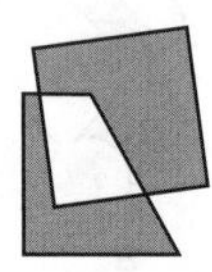
a

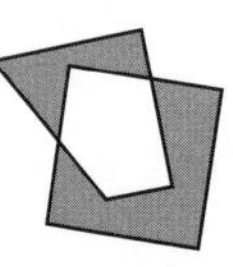
b

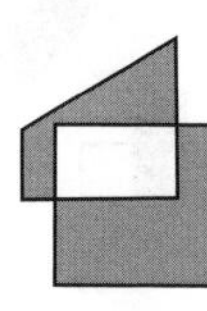
c

d

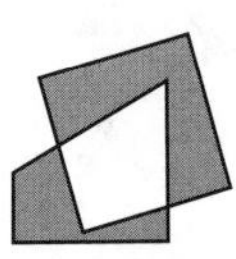
e

(____)

6. 7.

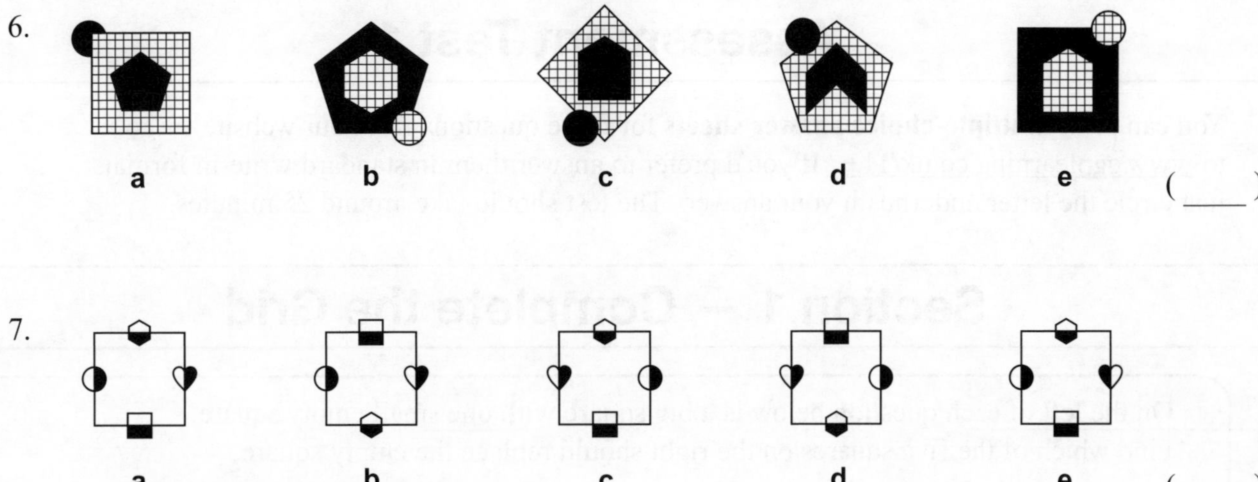

(____)

(____)

Complete the Pair

The first shape below is changed in some way to become the second. Choose the shape on the right that relates to the third shape in the same way that the second relates to the first.

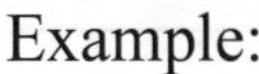

Example:

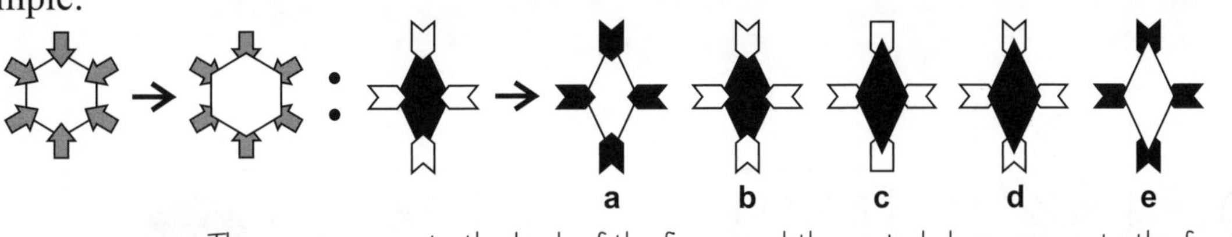

(d)

The arrows move to the back of the figure and the central shape moves to the front.

8.

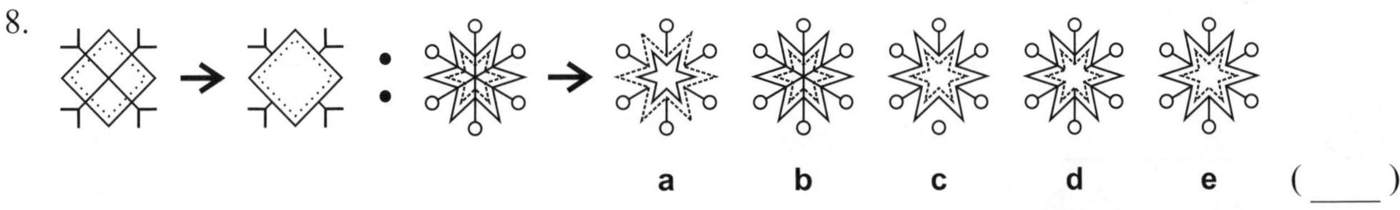

(____)

9.

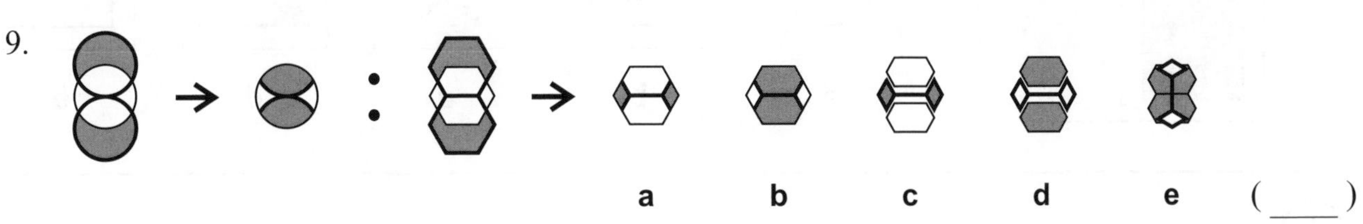

(____)

10.

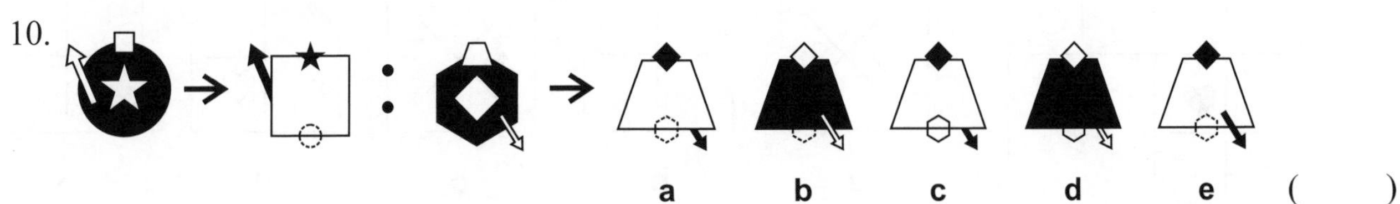

(____)

Assessment Test 1

You can print **multiple-choice answer sheets** for these questions from our website — go to www.cgplearning.co.uk/11+. If you'd prefer to answer them in standard write-in format, just circle the letter underneath your answer. The test should take around 25 minutes.

Section 1 — Complete the Grid

On the left of each question below is a big square with one small empty square. Find which of the five squares on the right should replace the empty square.

Example:

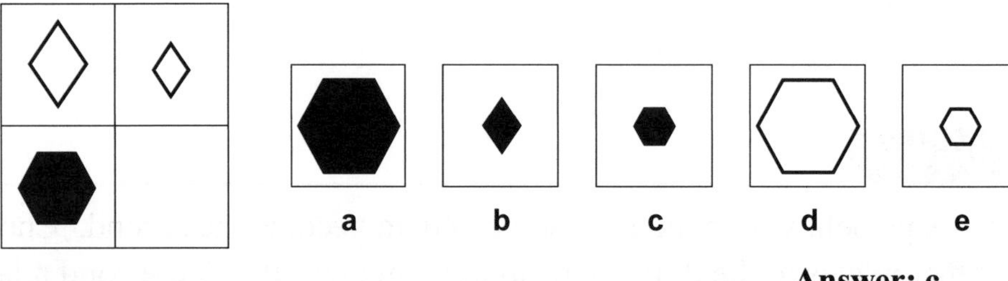

Answer: c

1

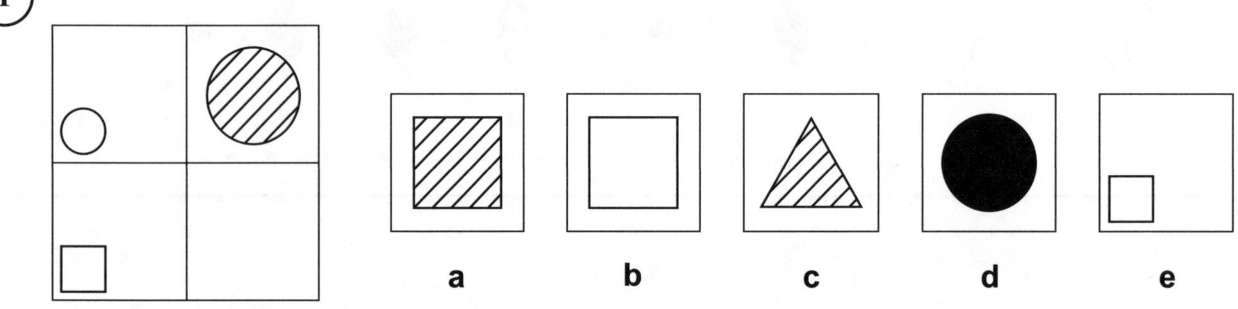

2

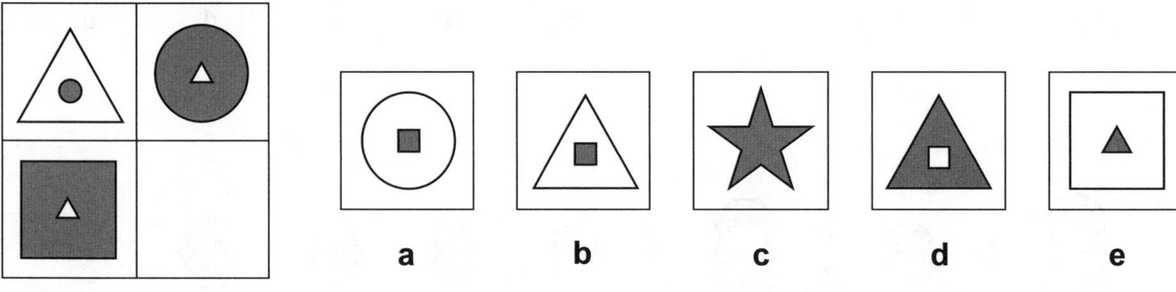

3

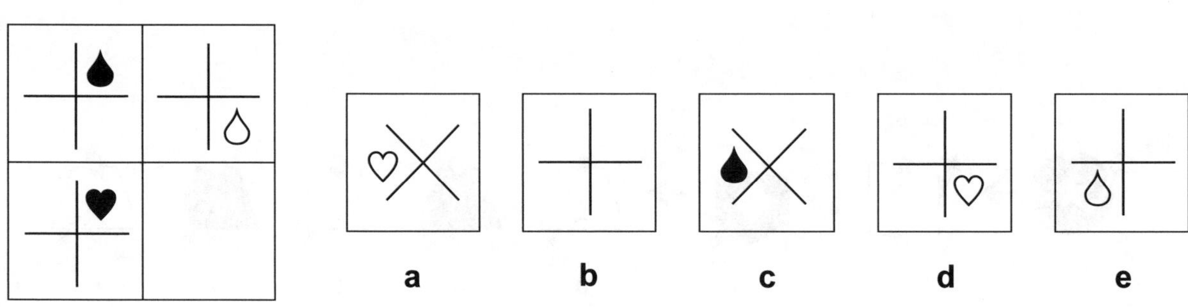

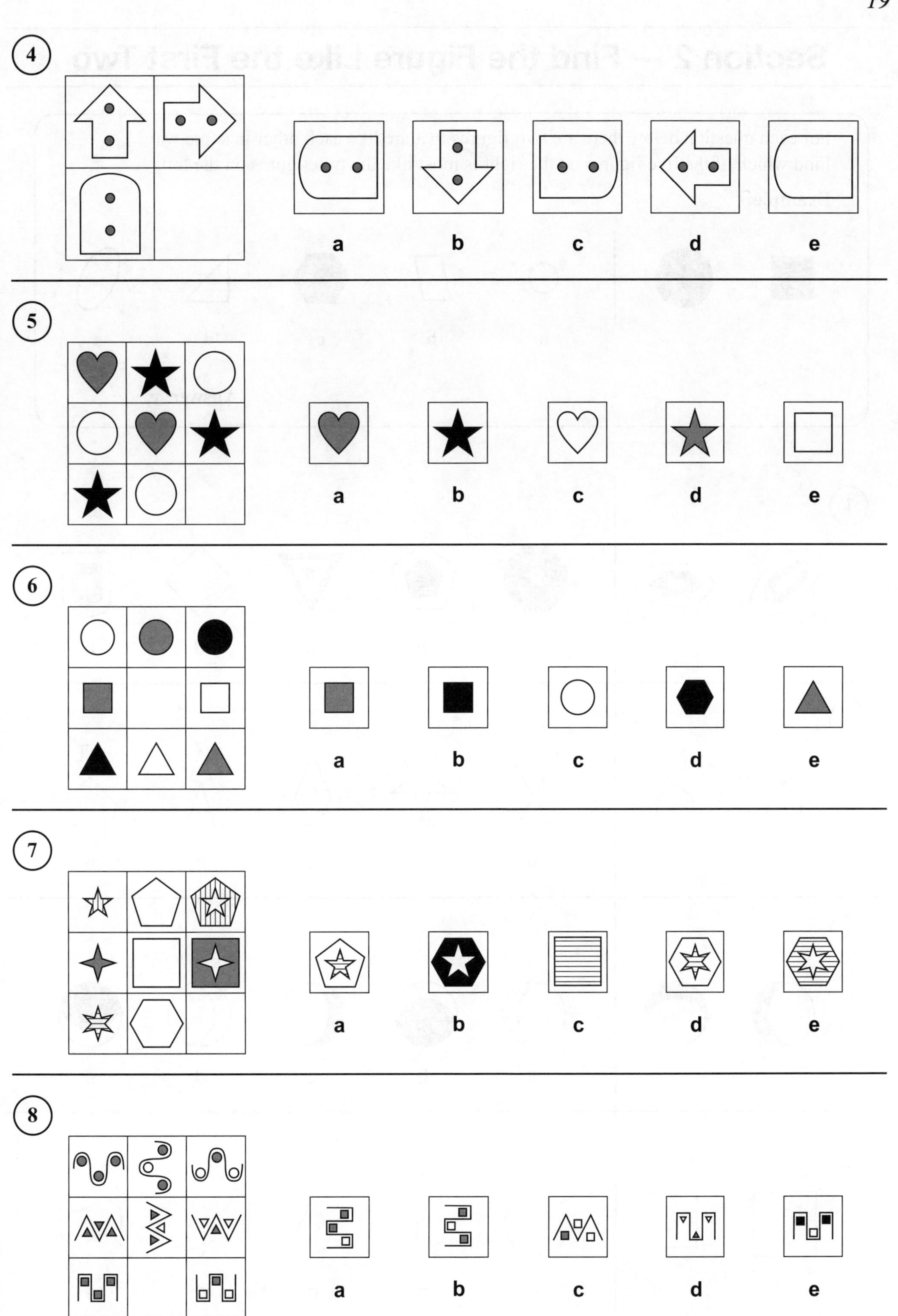

/ 8

Section 2 — Find the Figure Like the First Two

For each question below there are two figures that are like each other in some way.
Find which of the five figures on the right is most like the two figures on the left.

Example:

a b c d e

Answer: c

 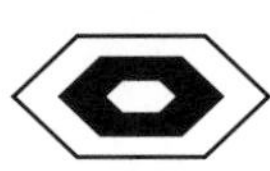  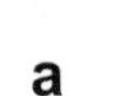   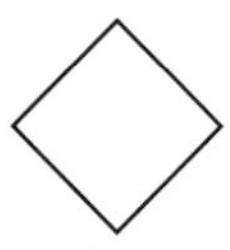 

a b c d e

(2)

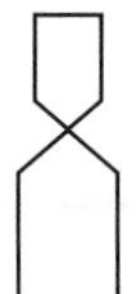 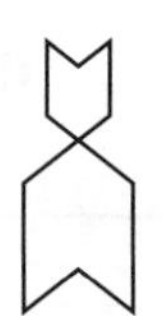    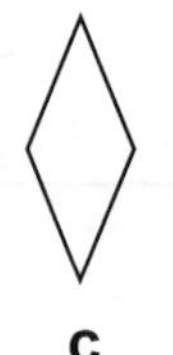  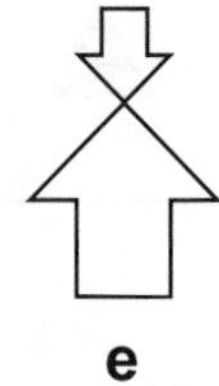

a b c d e

(3)

  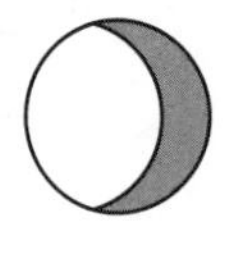    

a b c d e

(4)

 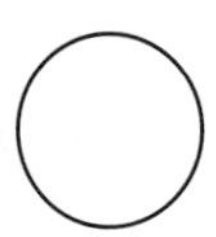  

a b c d e

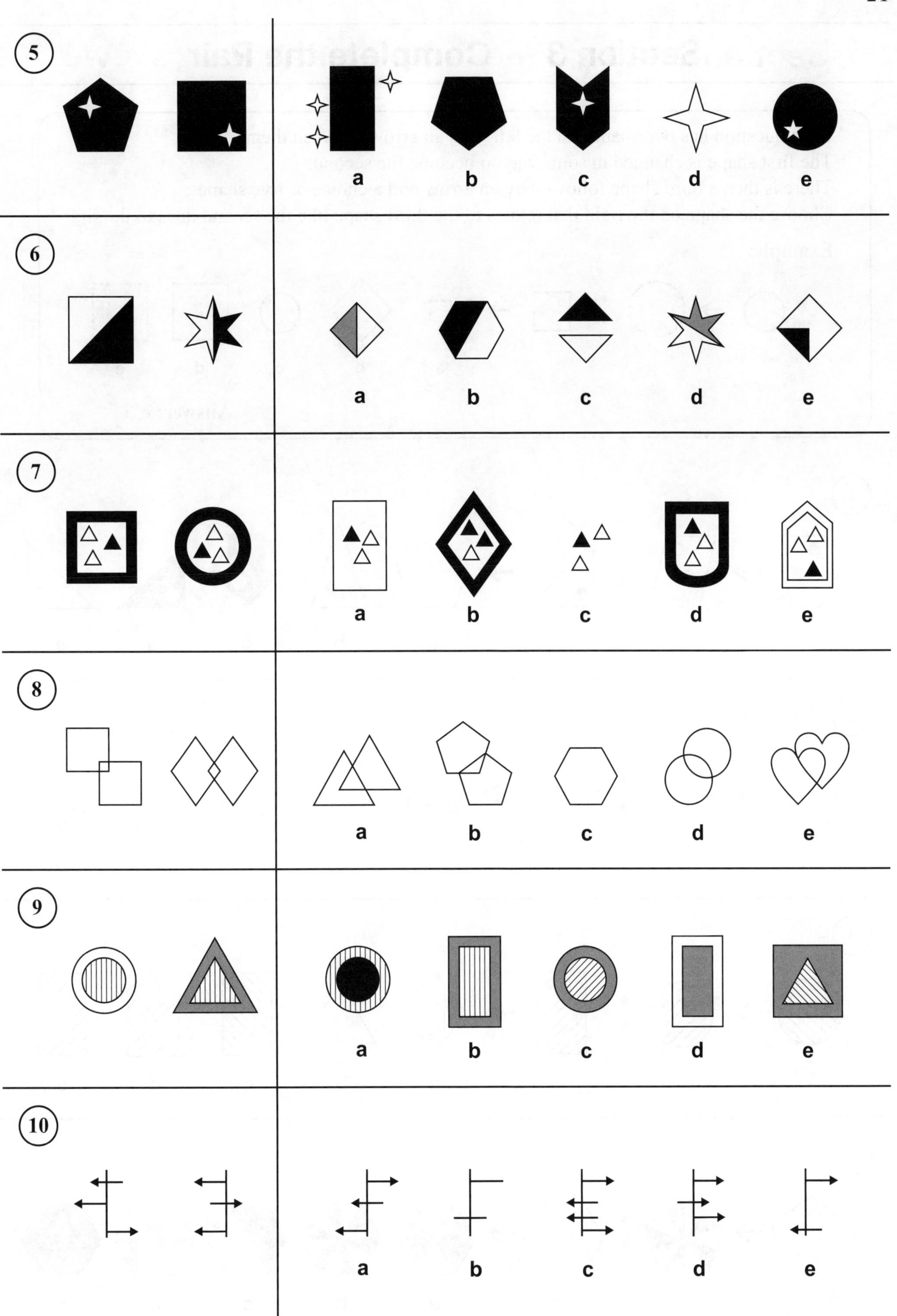

/ 10

Section 3 — Complete the Pair

Each question has two shapes on the left with an arrow between them.
The first shape is changed in some way to become the second.
There is then a third shape followed by an arrow and a choice of five shapes.
Choose the shape on the right that relates to the third shape like the second does to the first.

Example:

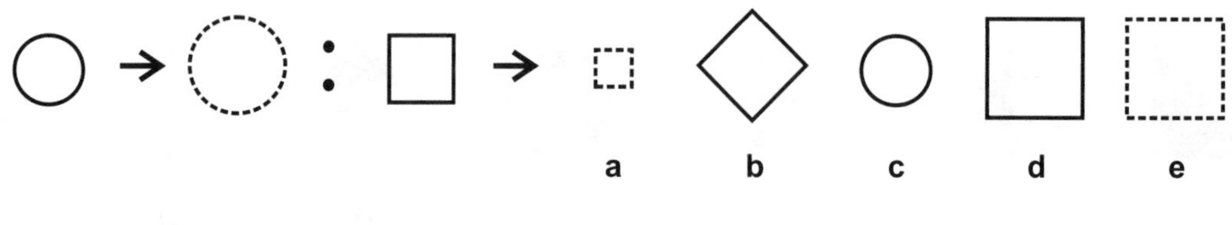

Answer: e

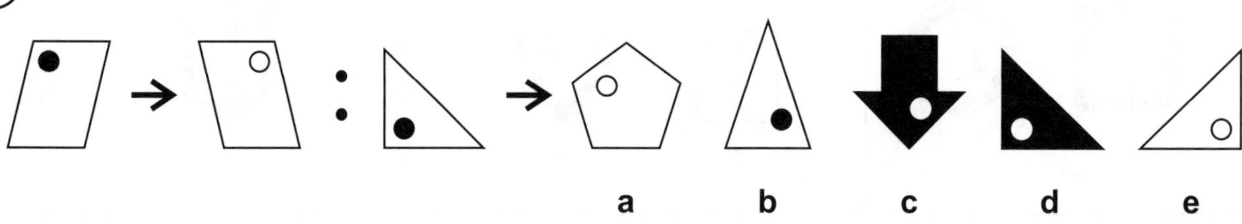

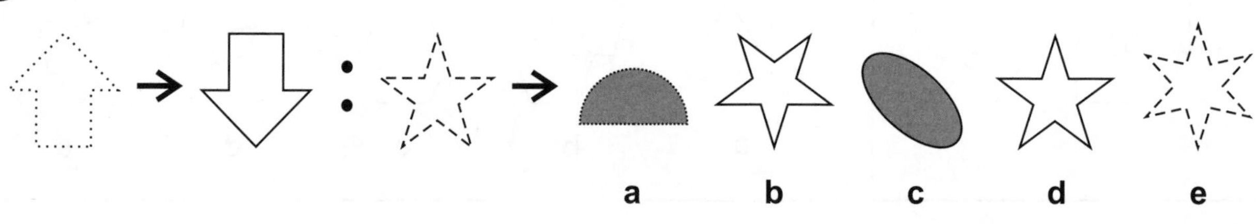

3

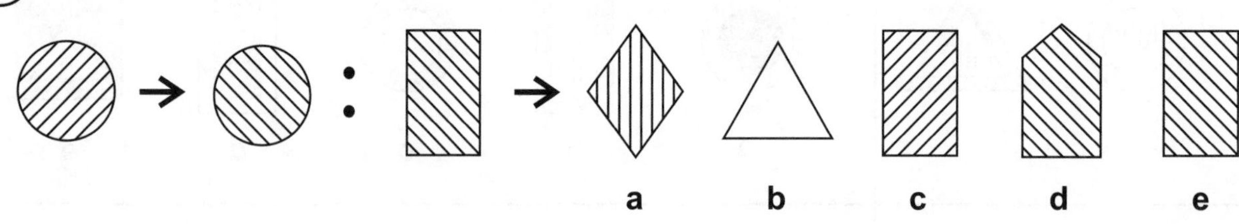

4

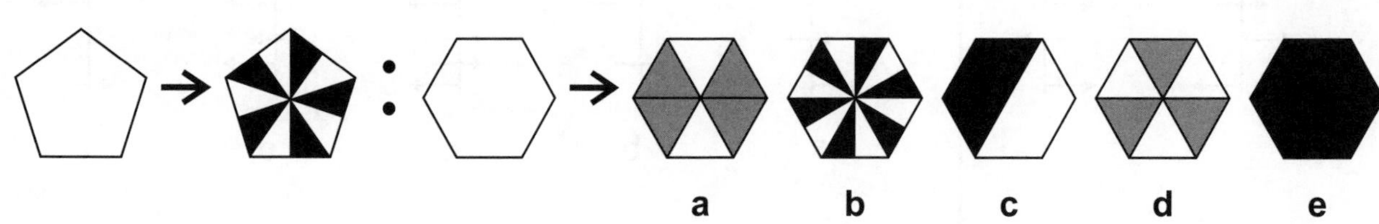

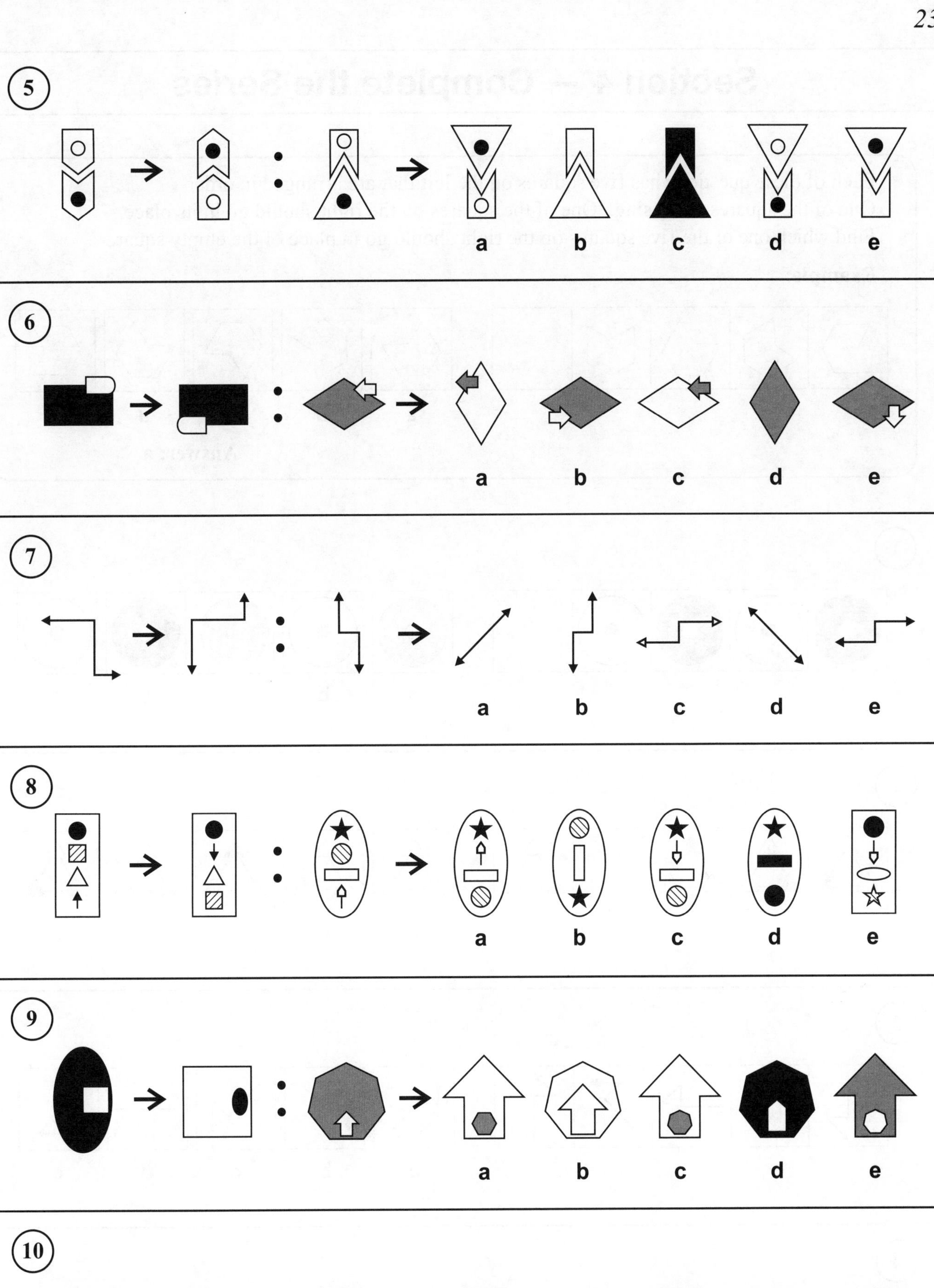

/ 10

Section 4 — Complete the Series

Each of these questions has five squares on the left that are arranged in order.
One of the squares is missing. One of the squares on the right should go in its place.
Find which one of the five squares on the right should go in place of the empty square.

Example:

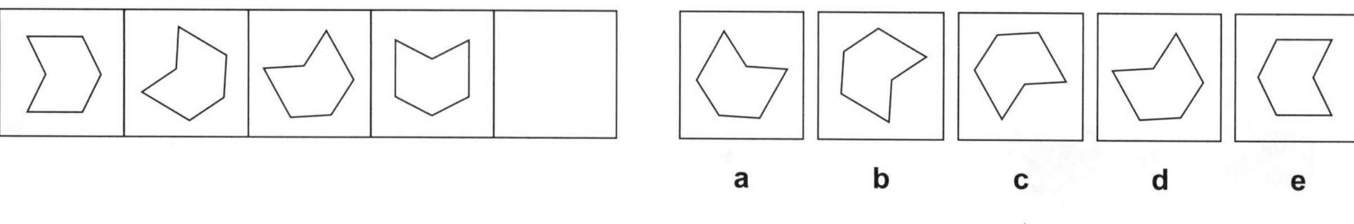

Answer: a

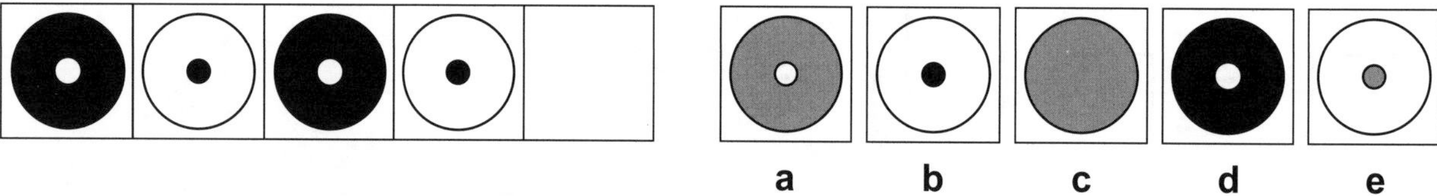

2

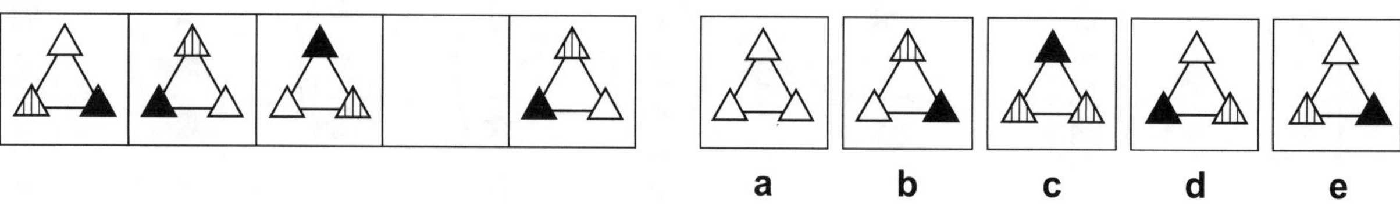

3

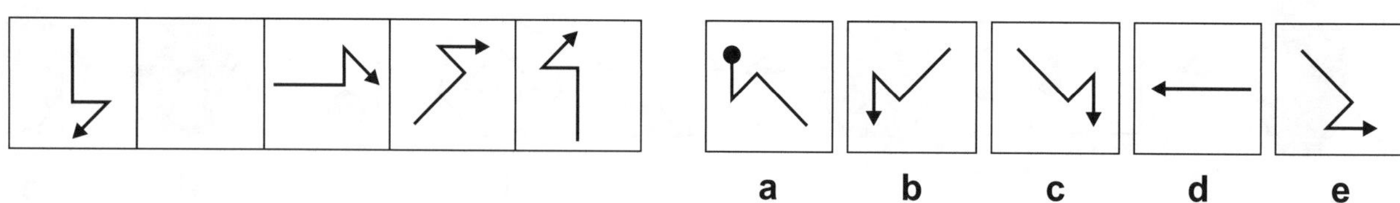

4

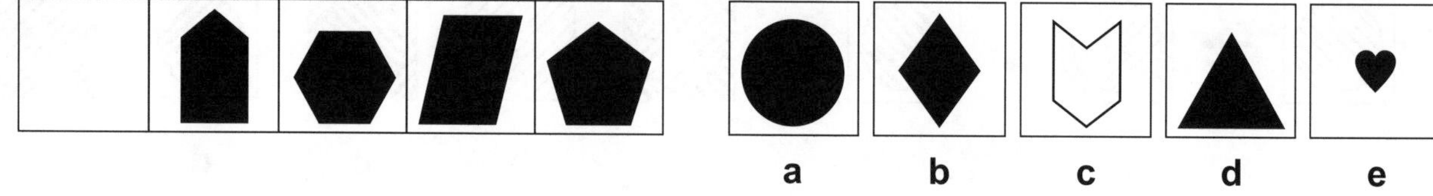

5

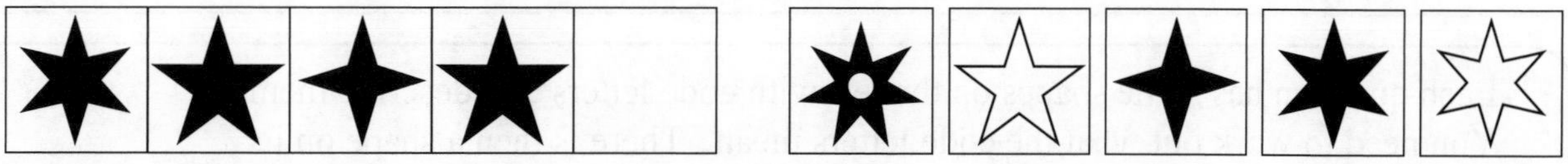

a b c d e

6

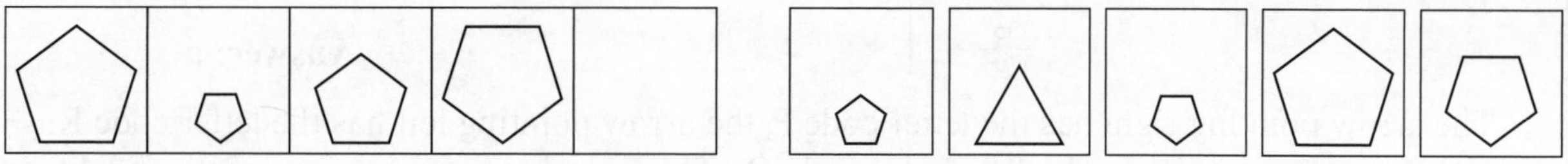

a b c d e

7

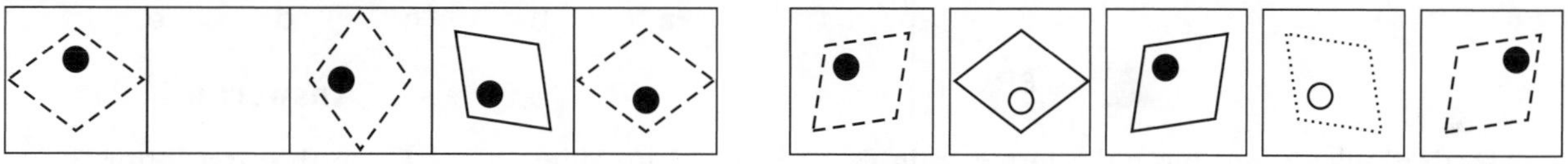

a b c d e

8

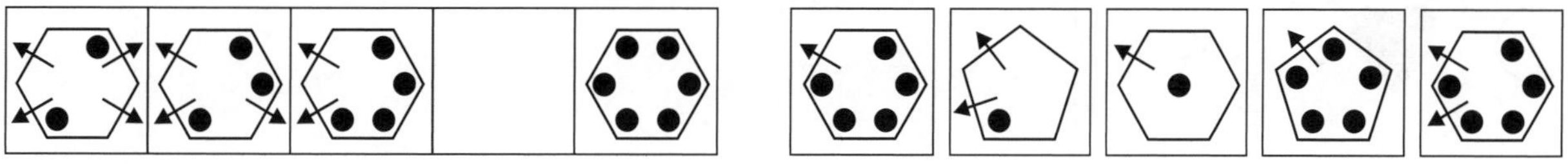

a b c d e

9

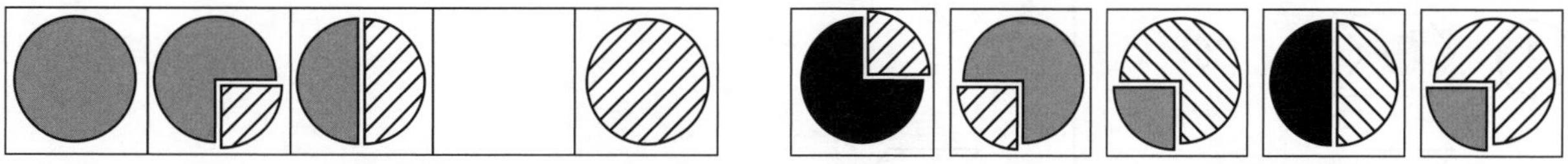

a b c d e

10

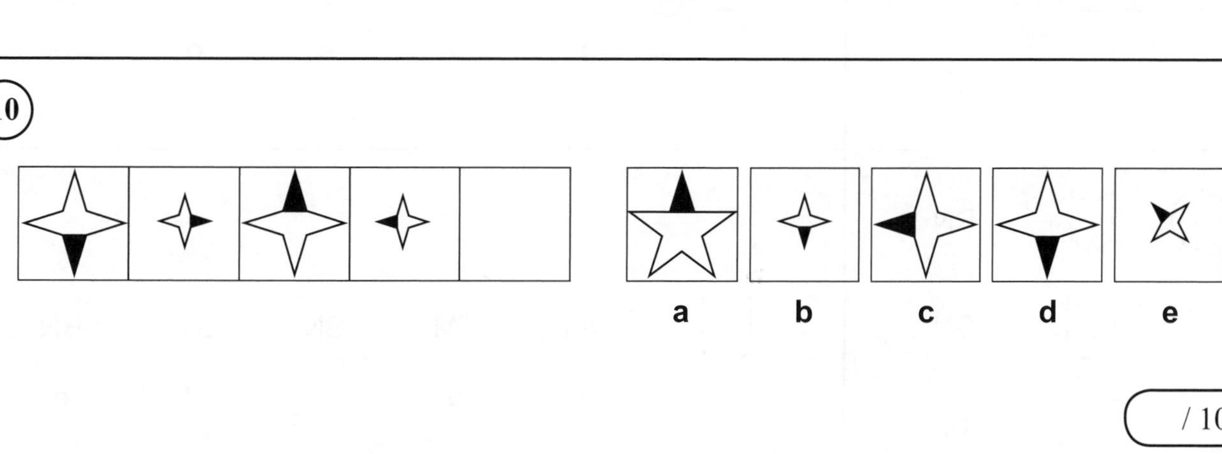

a b c d e

/ 10

Section 5 — Vertical Code

Each question has some shapes on the left with code letters that describe them. You need to work out what the code letters mean. There is then a shape on its own next to a choice of five codes. Work out which code describes this shape.

Example:

P

Q

R

P	Q	T	S	R
a	b	c	d	e

Answer: a

The arrow pointing right has the letter code P, the arrow pointing left has the letter code R, and the arrow pointing up has the letter code Q. The new shape is an arrow pointing right, so the code must be P and the answer is a.

Example:

BT

CS

BR

BC	CR	CT	BS	BR
a	b	c	d	e

Answer: d

Both black shapes have the letter code B, and the white shape has a C, so the first letter is for shading. The second letter code must be the code for shape. T stands for a pentagon, S for a circle and R for a triangle. The new shape must have a B because it is black, and an S because it is a circle. The code must be BS and the answer is d.

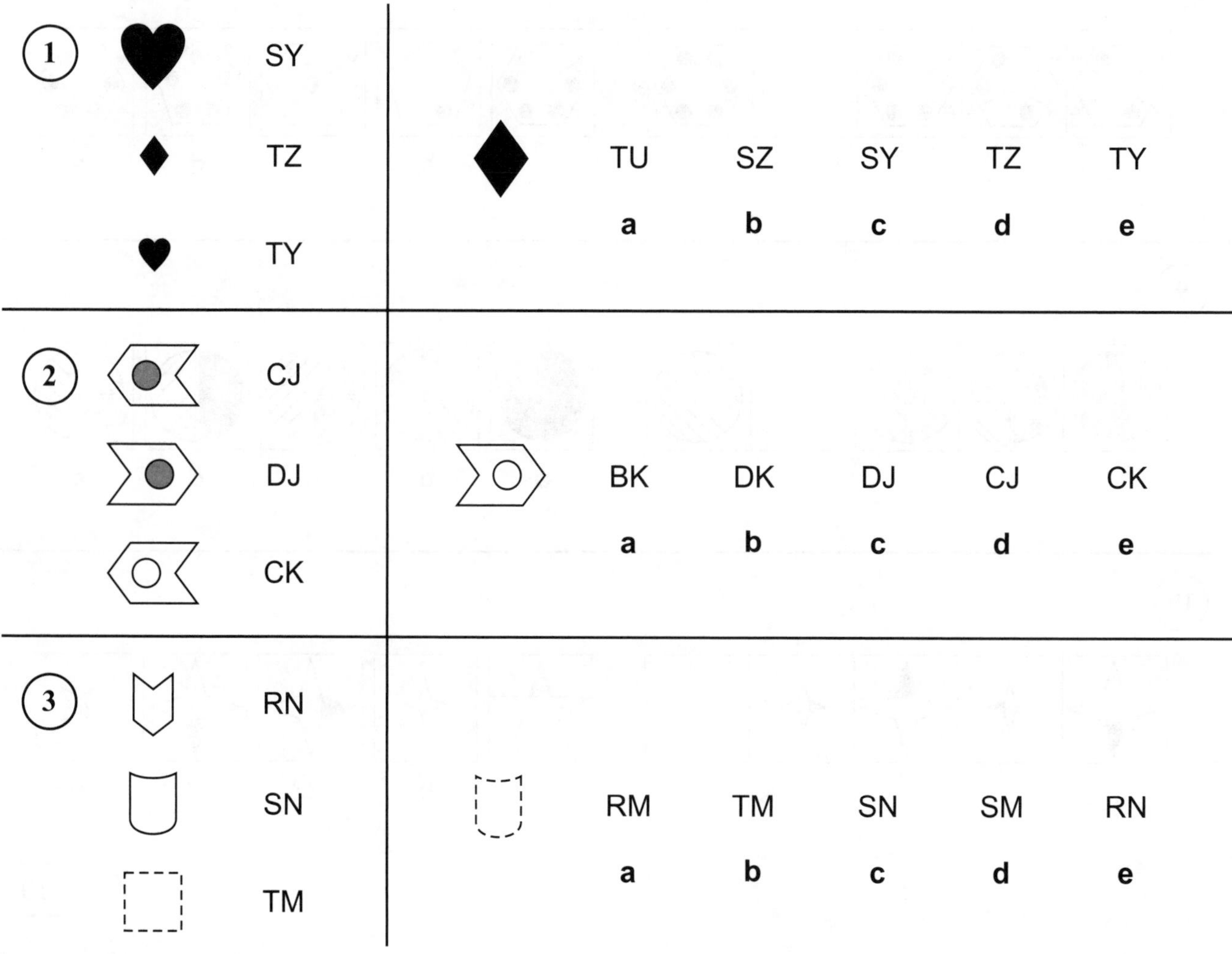

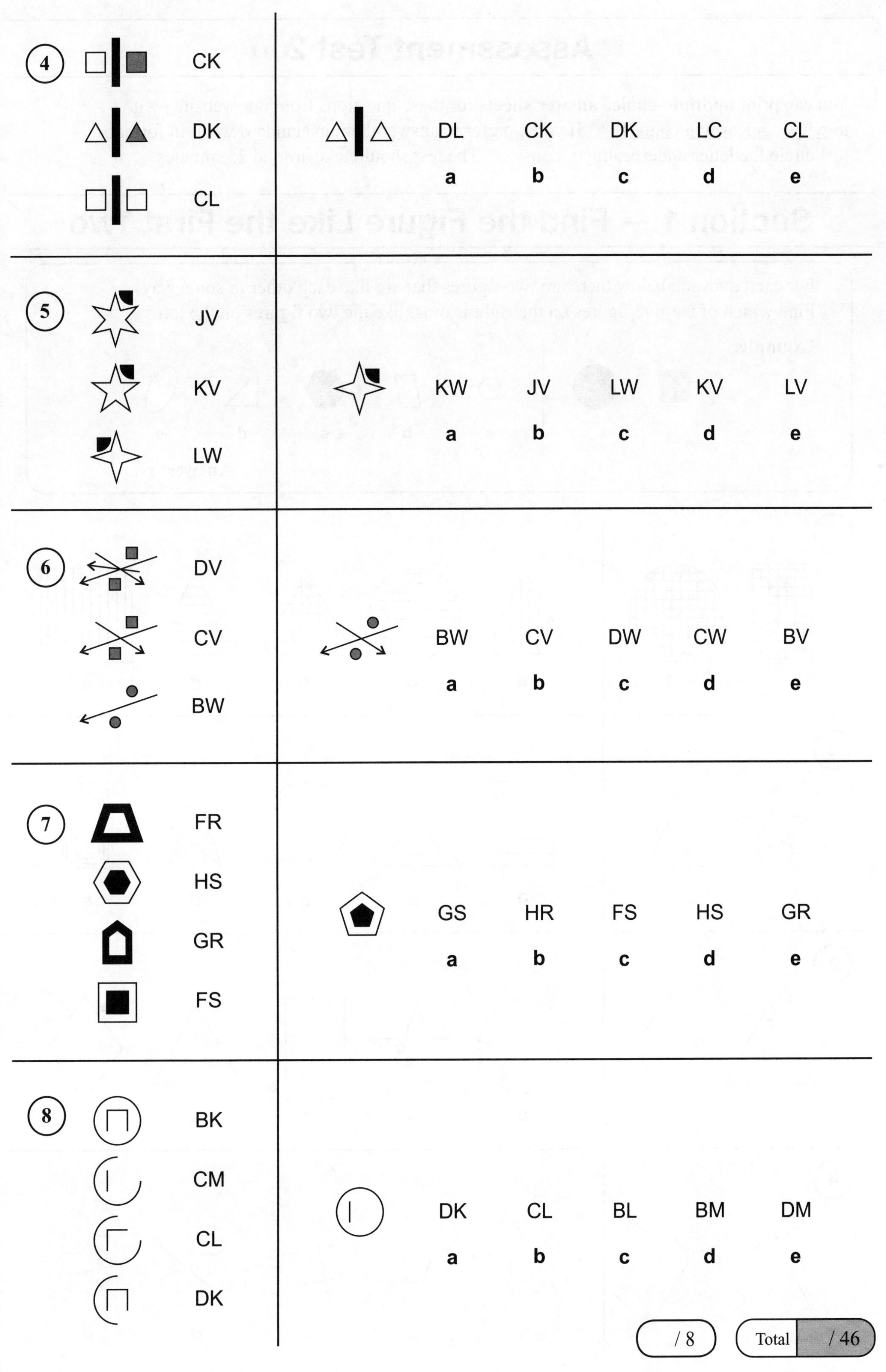
4
CK
DK
CL
DL
CK
DK
LC
CL
a
b
c
d
e
5
JV
KV
LW
KW
JV
LW
KV
LV
a
b
c
d
e
6
DV
CV
BW
BW
CV
DW
CW
BV
a
b
c
d
e
7
FR
HS
GR
FS
GS
HR
FS
HS
GR
a
b
c
d
e
8
BK
CM
CL
DK
DK
CL
BL
BM
DM
a
b
c
d
e
/ 8
Total
/ 46

END OF TEST

Assessment Test 2

You can print **multiple-choice answer sheets** for these questions from our website — go to www.cgplearning.co.uk/11+. If you'd prefer to answer them in standard write-in format, just circle the letter underneath your answer. The test should take around 25 minutes.

Section 1 — Find the Figure Like the First Two

For each question below there are two figures that are like each other in some way. Find which of the five figures on the right is most like the two figures on the left.

Example:

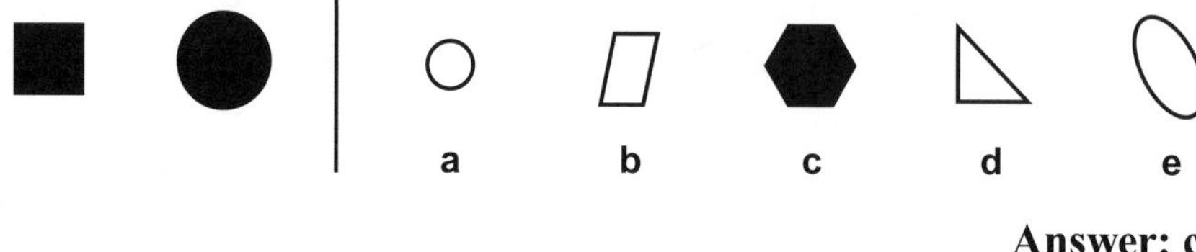

Answer: c

1

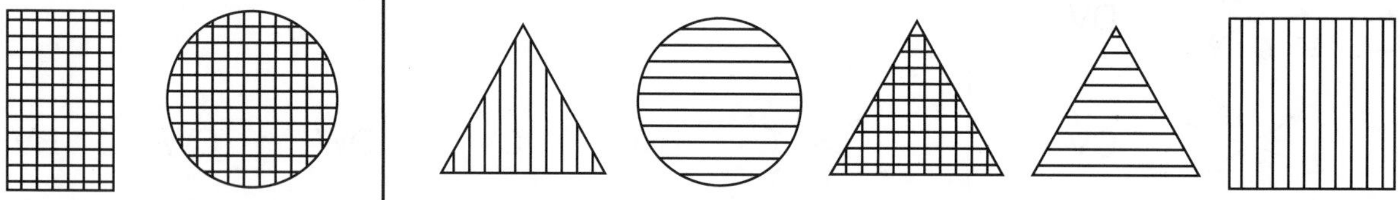

a b c d e

2

a b c d e

3

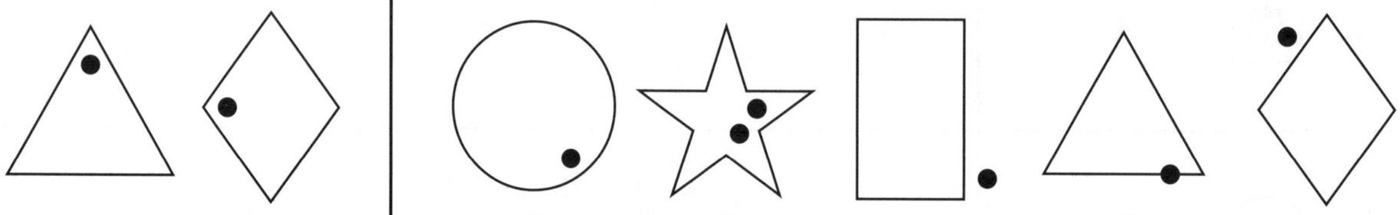

a b c d e

4

a b c d e

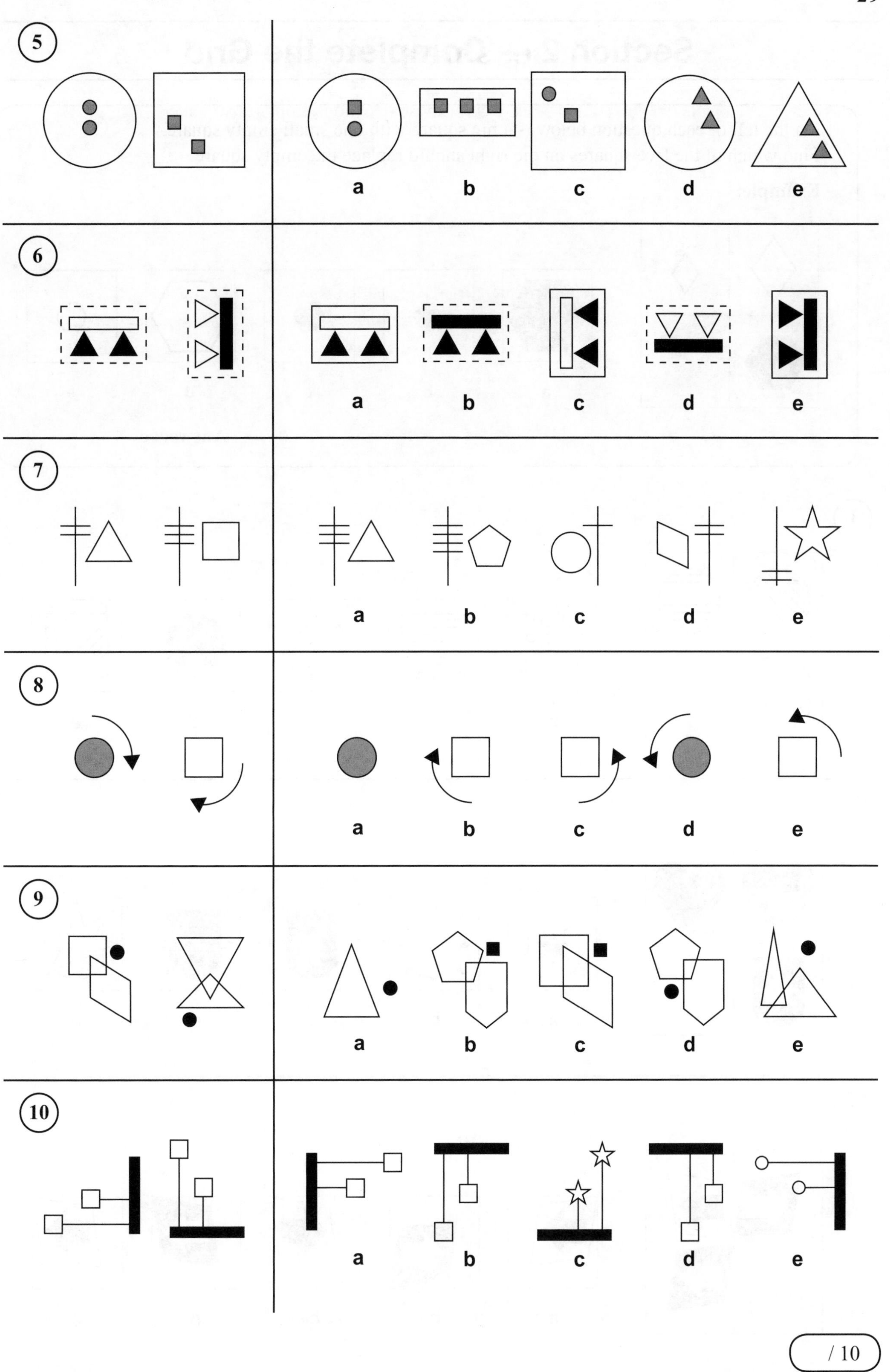

/ 10

Section 2 — Complete the Grid

On the left of each question below is a big square with one small empty square.
Find which of the five squares on the right should replace the empty square.

Example:

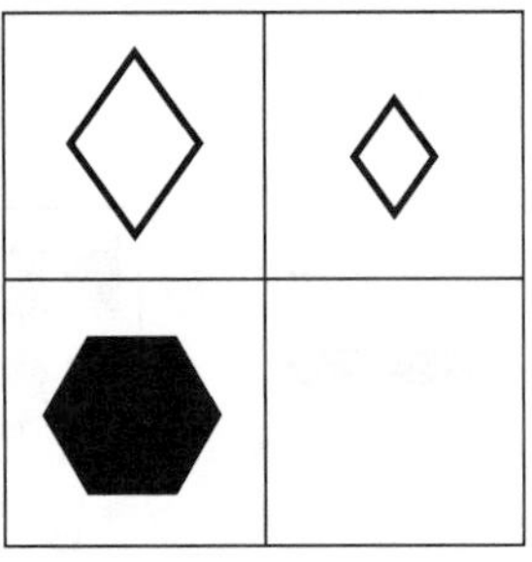

a

b

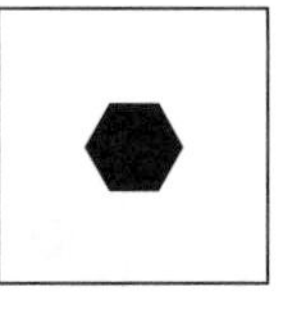

c

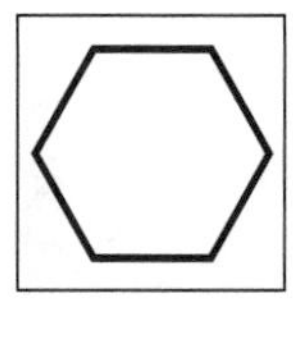

d

e

Answer: c

(1)

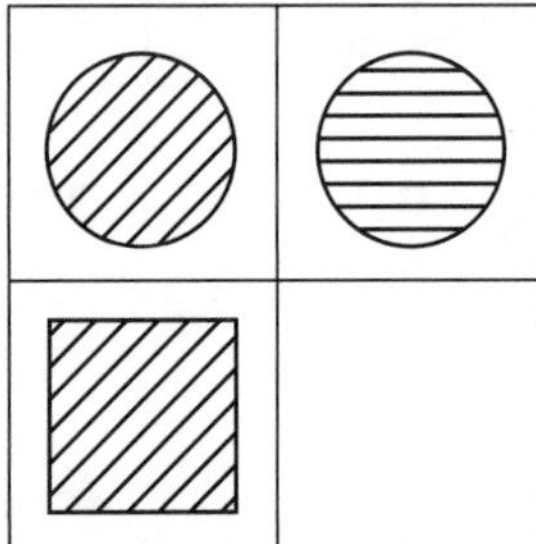

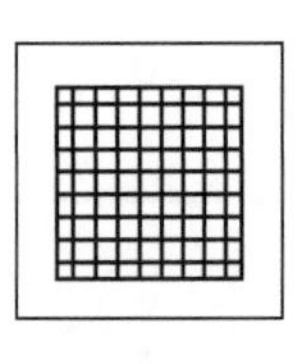

a

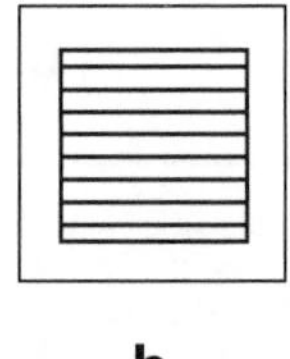

b

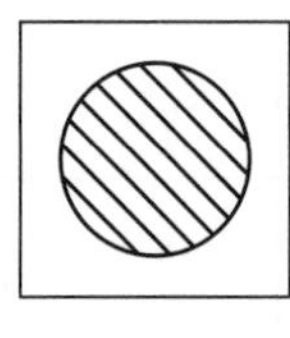

c

d

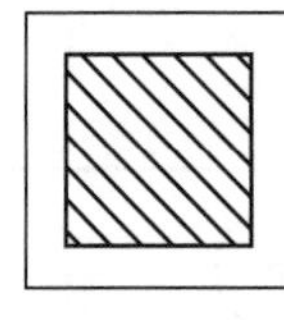

e

(2)

a

b

c

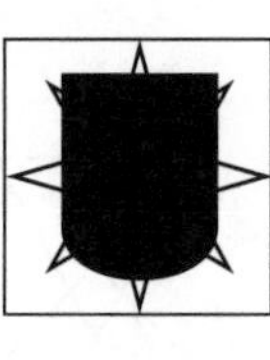

d

e

(3)

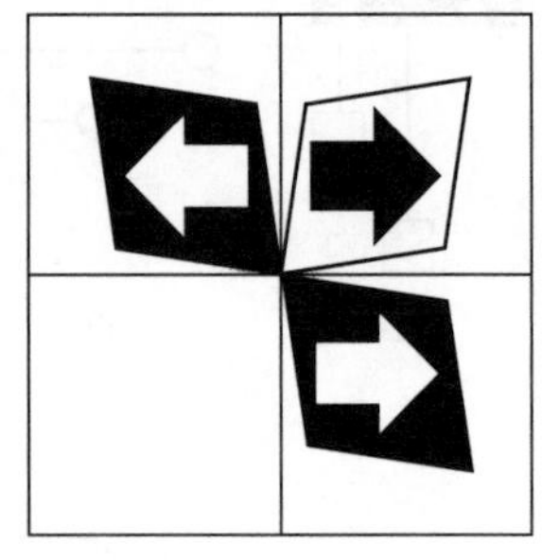

a

b

c

d

e

4

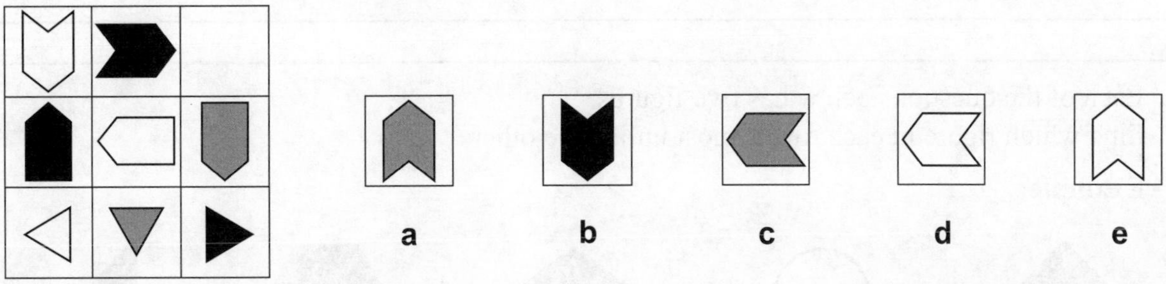

a b c d e

5

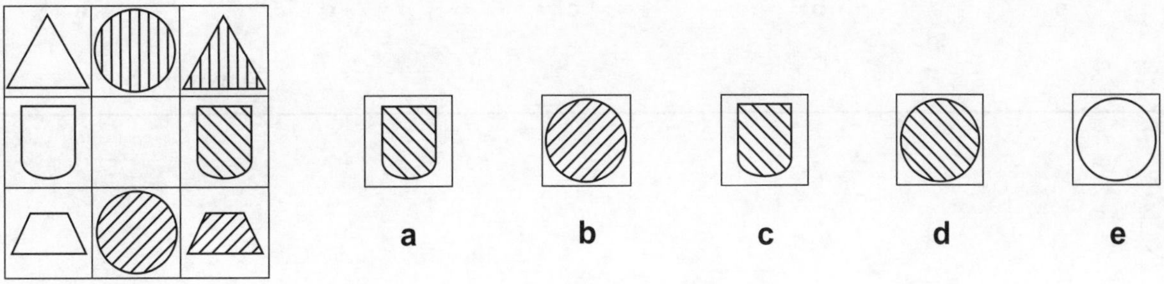

a b c d e

6

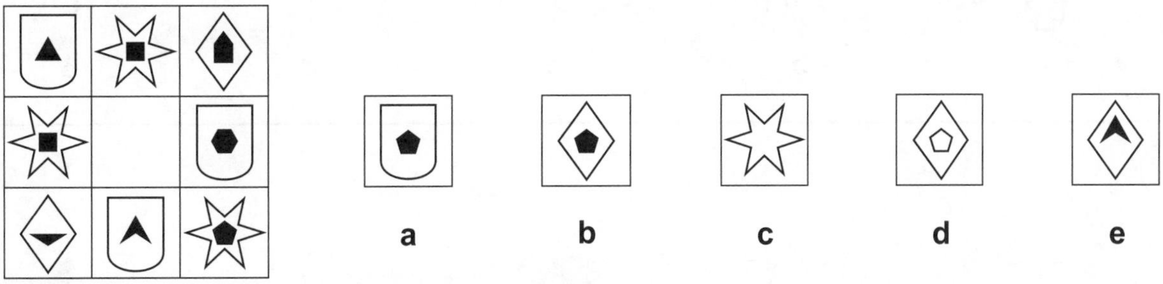

a b c d e

7

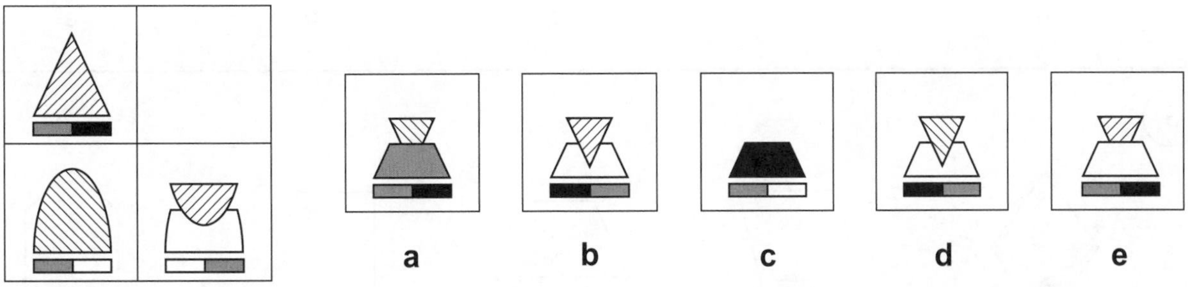

a b c d e

8

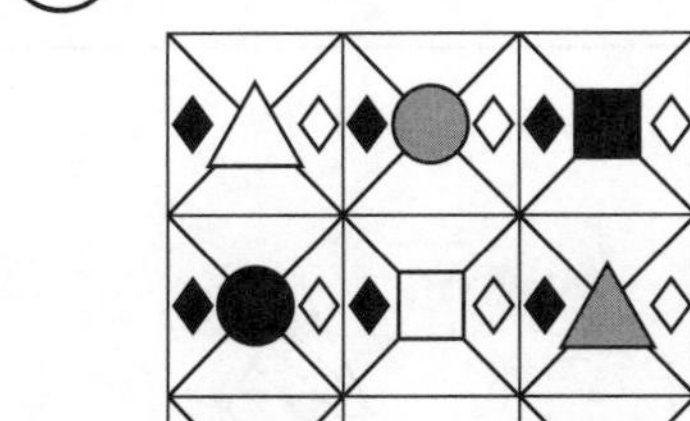

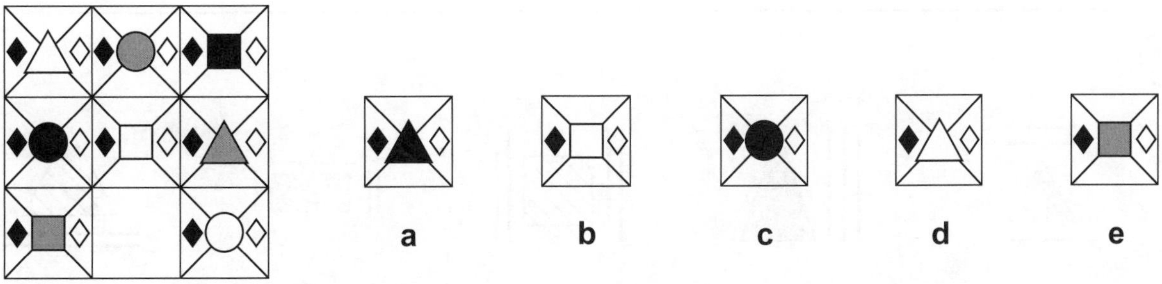

a

b

c

d

e

/ 8

Section 3 — Odd One Out

Each of the questions below has five figures.
Find which figure in each row is most unlike the others.

Example:

a

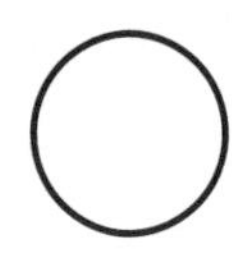
b

c

d

e

Answer: b

a

b

c

d

e

2

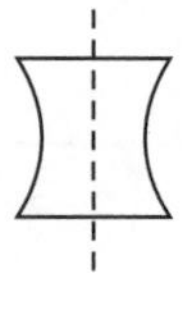
a

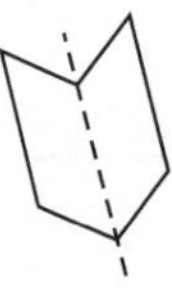
b

c

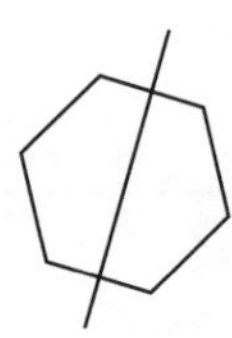
d

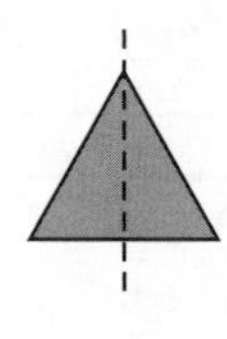
e

3

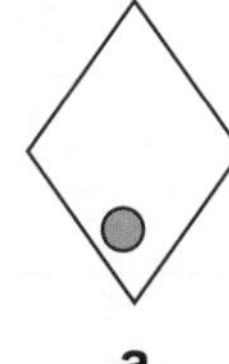
a

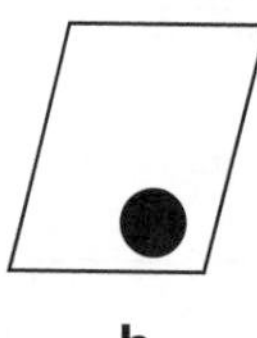
b

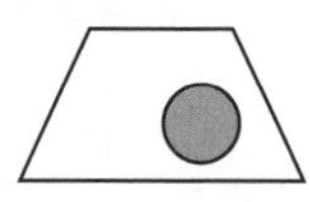
c

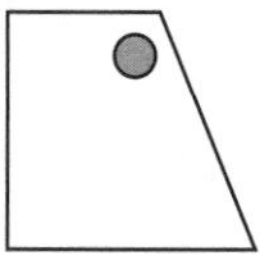
d

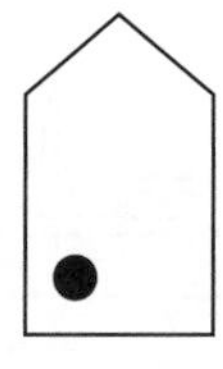
e

4

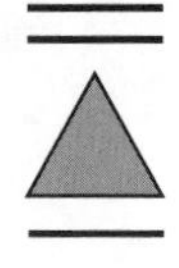
a

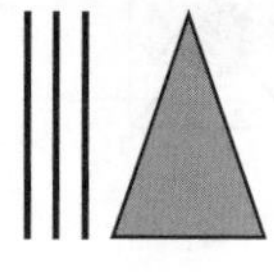
b

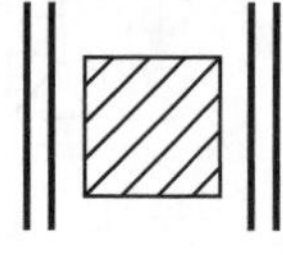
c

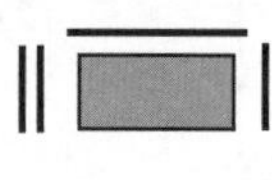
d

e

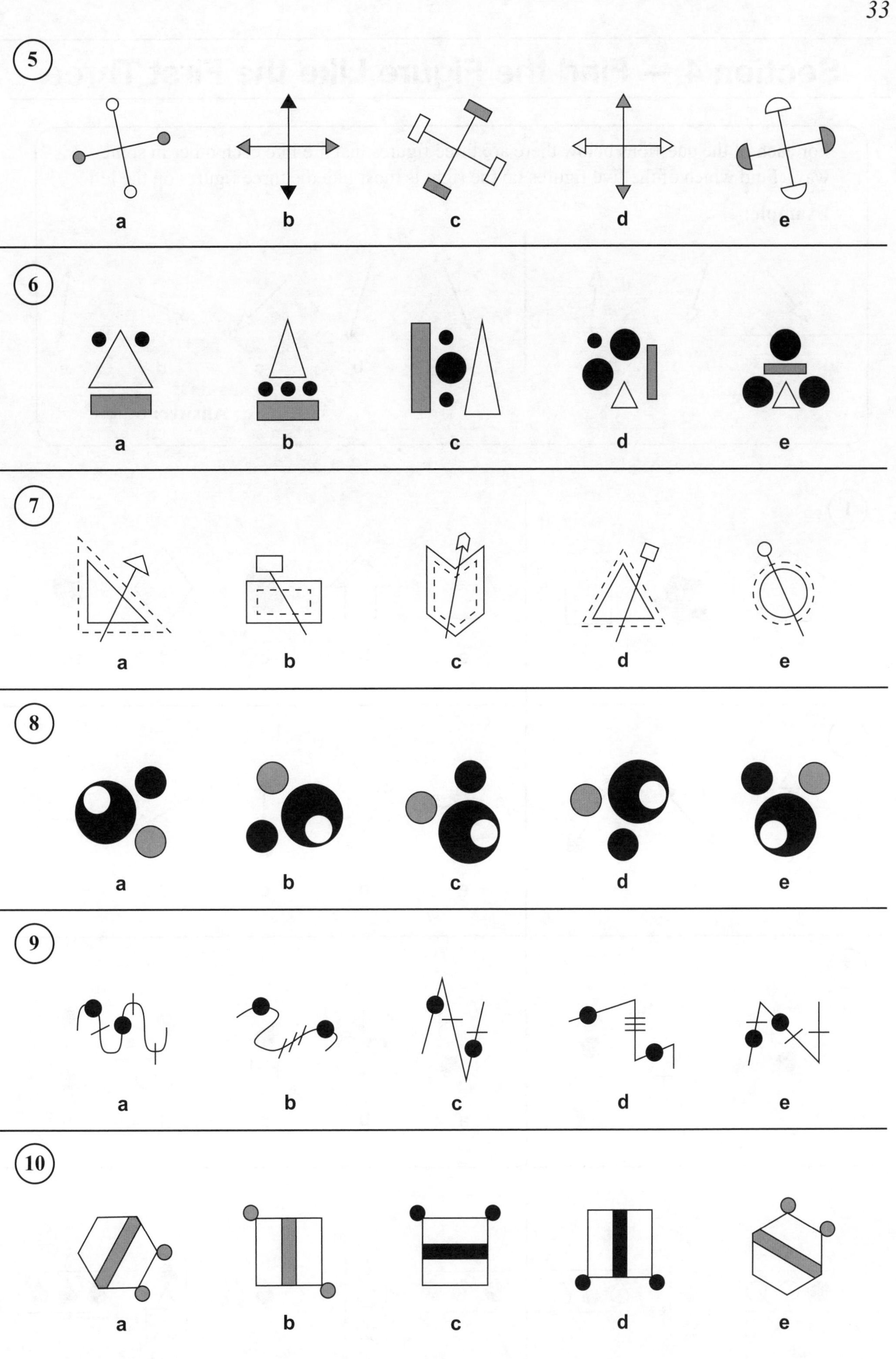

/ 10

Section 4 — Find the Figure Like the First Three

For each of the questions below there are three figures that are like each other in some way. Find which of the five figures on the right is most like the three figures on the left.

Example:

a
b
c
d
e

Answer: c

1

a
b
c
d
e

2

a
b
c
d
e

3

a
b
c
d
e

4

a
b
c
d
e

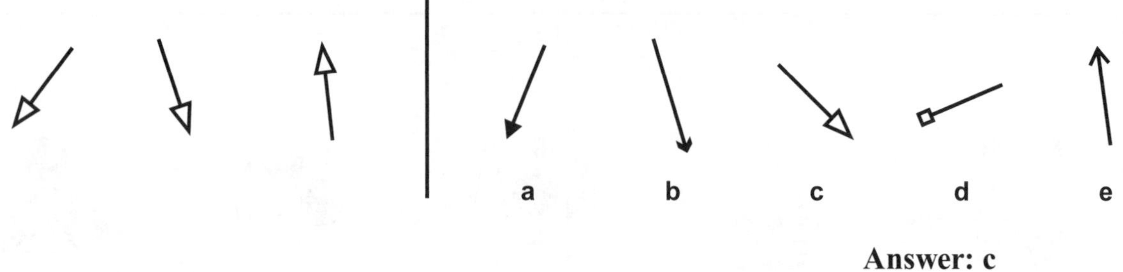

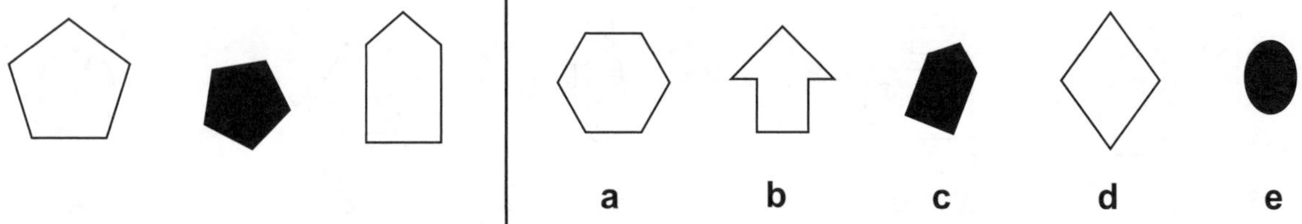

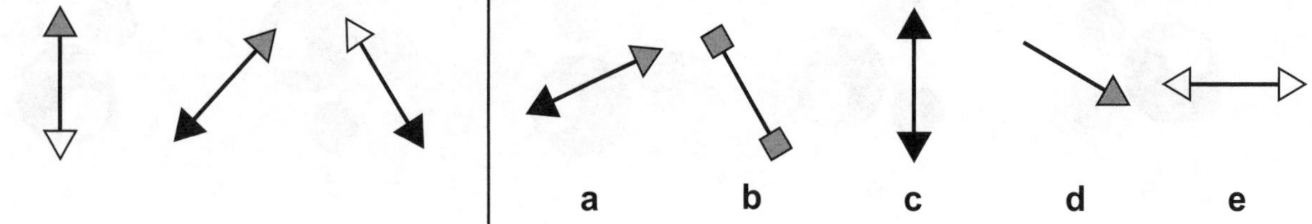

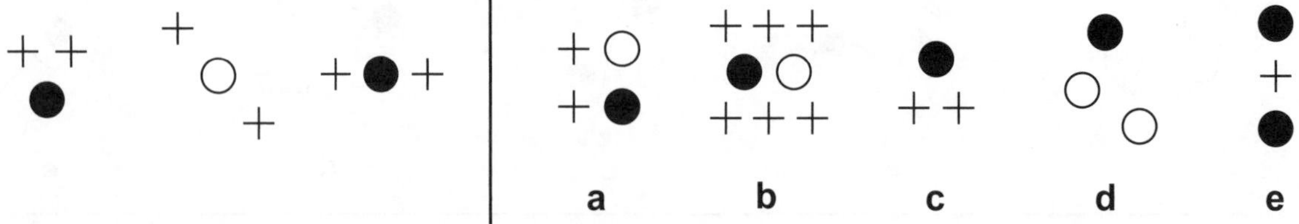

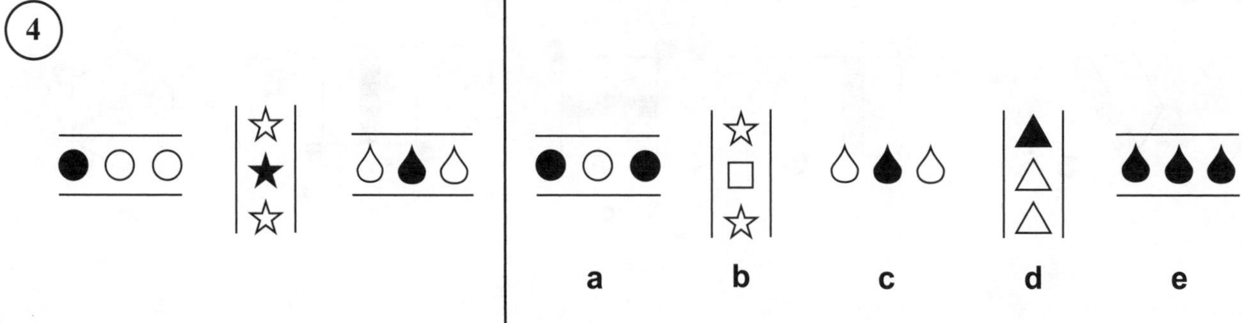

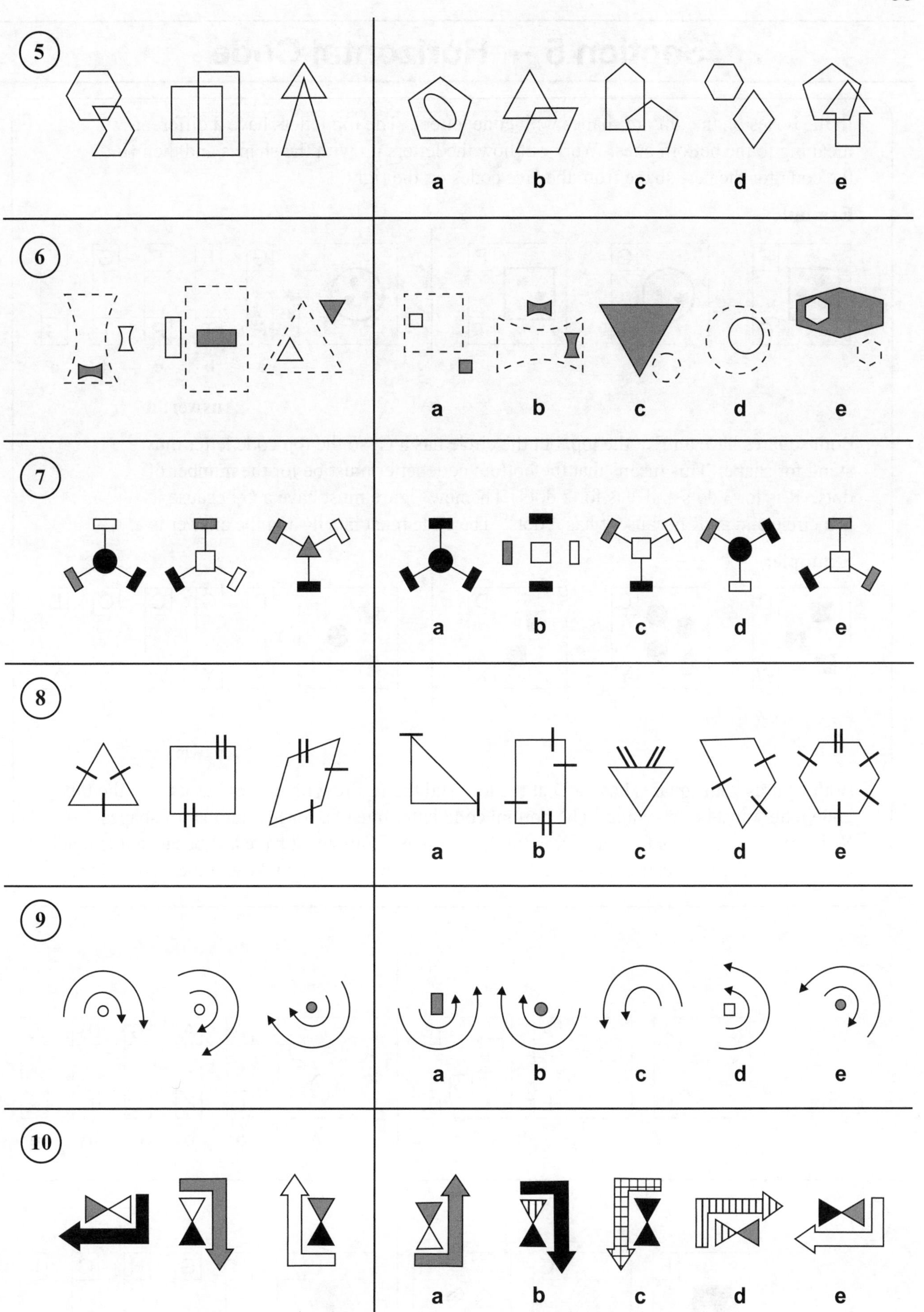

/ 10

Section 5 — Horizontal Code

In the boxes on the left are shapes with code letters. The top letters have a different meaning to the bottom ones. Work out how the letters go with the shapes and then find the code for the new shape from the five codes on the right.

Example:

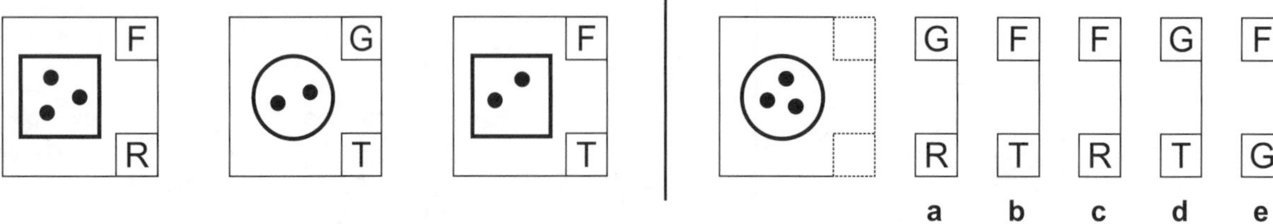

Answer: a

Both squares have an F at the top, but the circle has a G, so the top code letter must stand for shape. This means that the bottom code letter must be for the number of dots. R is for 3 dots and T is for 2 dots. The new figure must have a G because it is a circle and an R because it has 3 dots. The code must be GR and the answer is a.

Example:

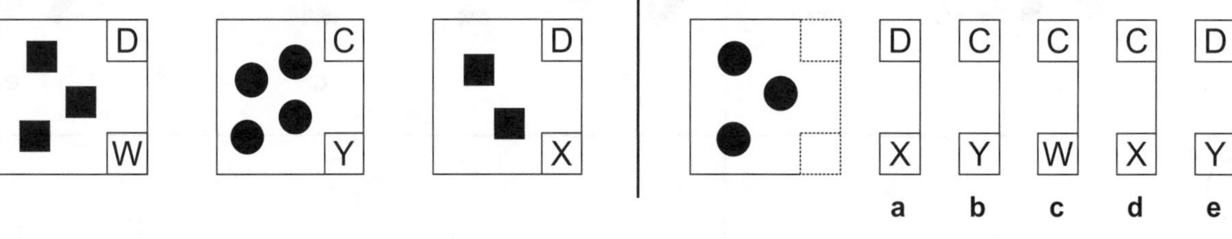

Answer: c

Both figures with squares have a D at the top, and the figure with circles has a C, so the top code letter must be for shape. The bottom code letter must be for the number of shapes. W is for 3 shapes, Y is for 4 and X is for 2. The new figure must have a C because it is made of circles and a W because there are 3 of them. The code must be CW and the answer is c.

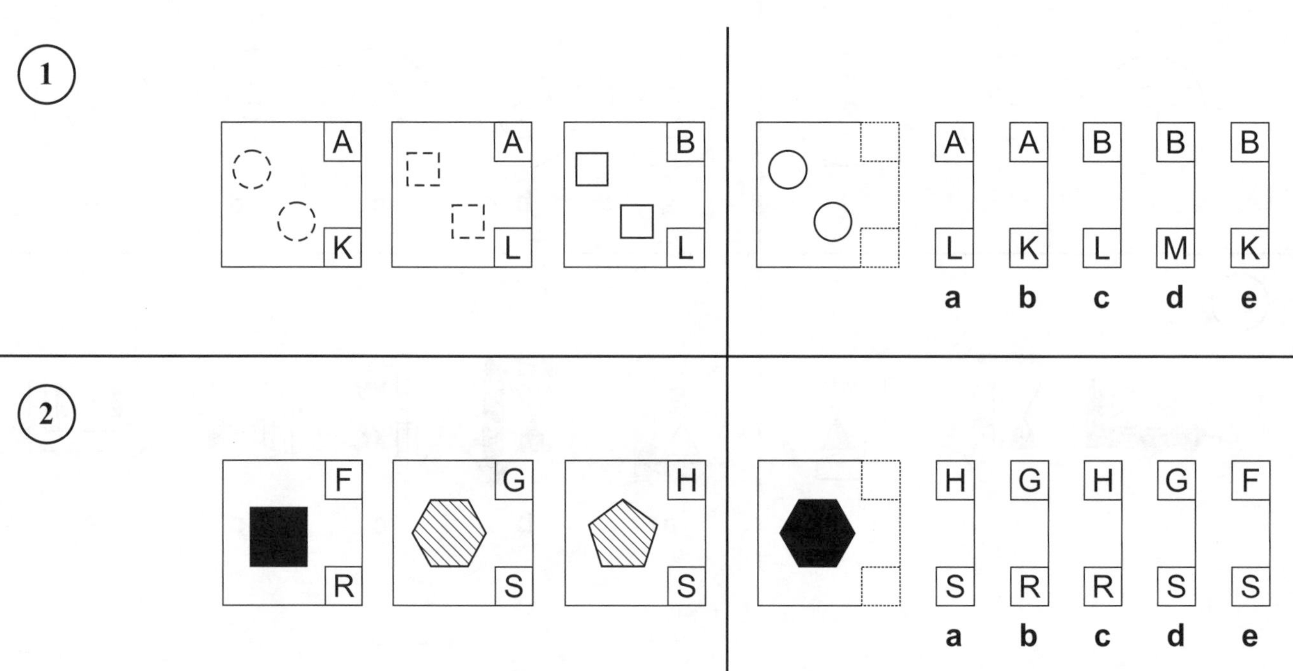

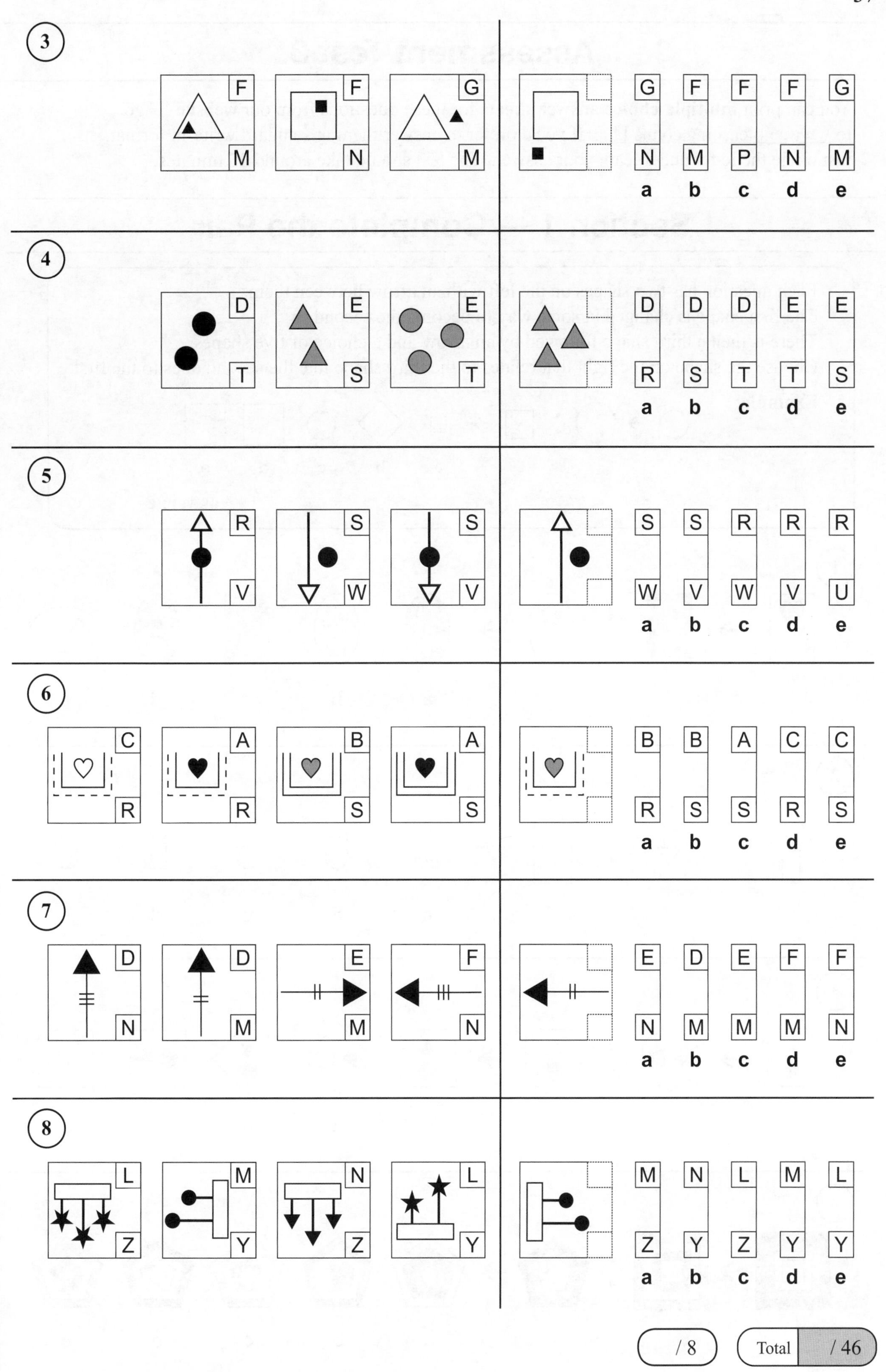

3
F
M
F
N
G
M
G N a
F M b
F P c
F N d
G M e
4
D
T
E
S
E
T
D R a
D S b
D T c
E T d
E S e
5
R
V
S
W
S
V
S W a
S V b
R W c
R V d
R U e
6
C
R
A
R
B
S
A
S
B R a
B S b
A S c
C R d
C S e
7
D
N
D
M
E
M
F
N
E N a
D M b
E M c
F M d
F N e
8
L
Z
M
Y
N
Z
L
Y
M Z a
N Y b
L Z c
M Y d
L Y e

/ 8

Total / 46

Assessment Test 3

You can print **multiple-choice answer sheets** for these questions from our website — go to www.cgplearning.co.uk/11+. If you'd prefer to answer them in standard write-in format, just circle the letter underneath your answer. The test should take around 25 minutes.

Section 1 — Complete the Pair

Each question has two shapes on the left with an arrow between them.
The first shape is changed in some way to become the second.
There is then a third shape followed by an arrow and a choice of five shapes.
Choose the shape on the right that relates to the third shape like the second does to the first.

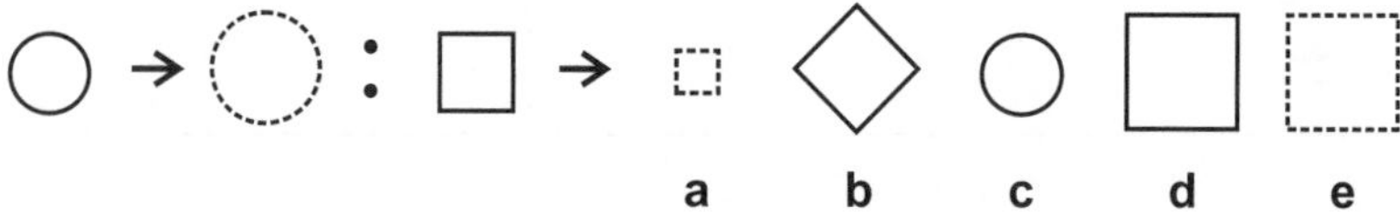

a b c d e

Answer: e

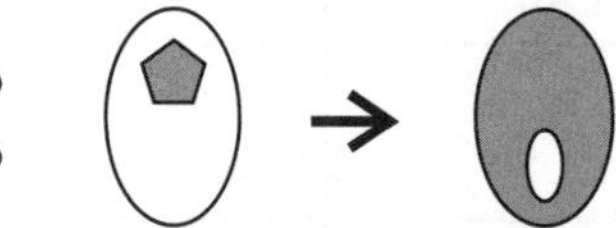
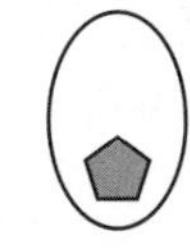
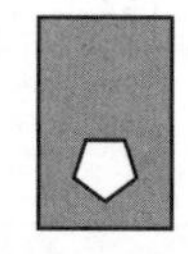
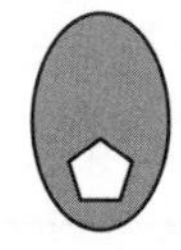
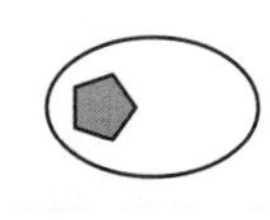

a b c d e

2

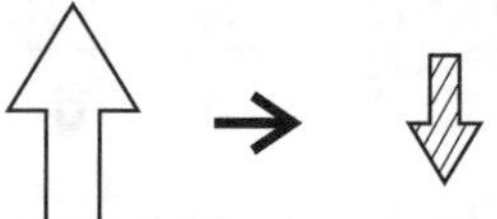
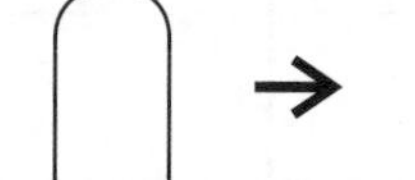

a b c d e

3

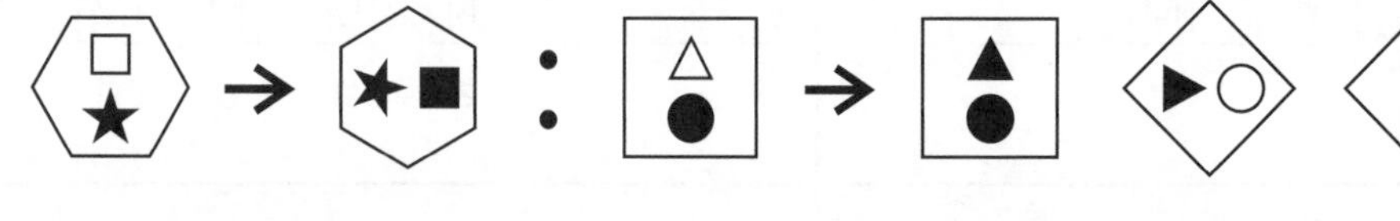

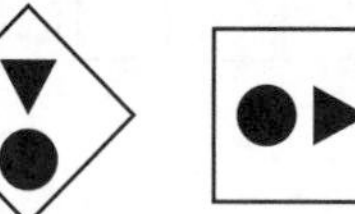
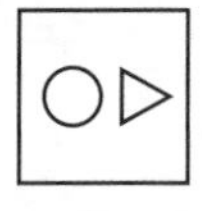

a b c d e

4

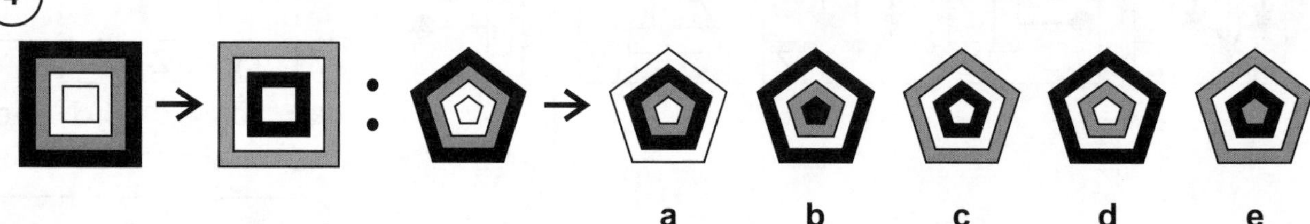

a b c d e

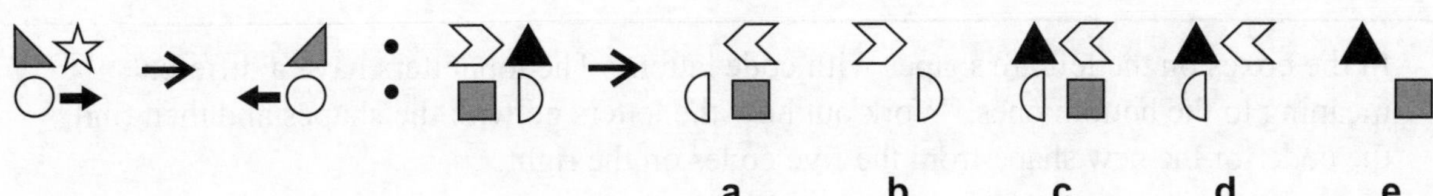

a b c d e

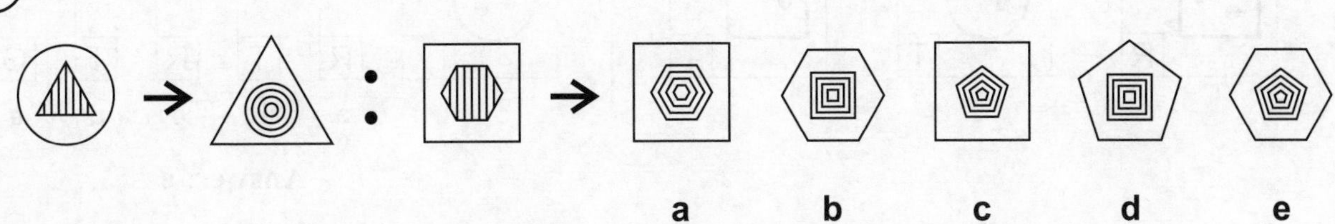

a b c d e

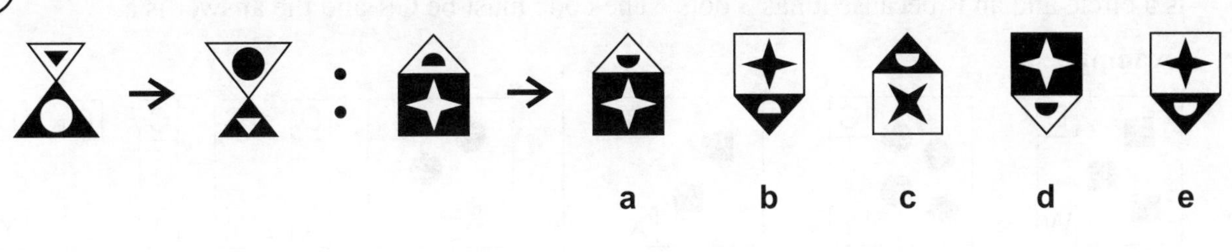

a b c d e

8

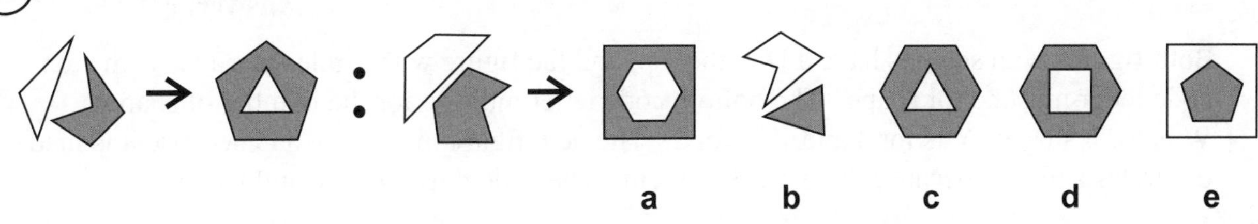

a b c d e

9

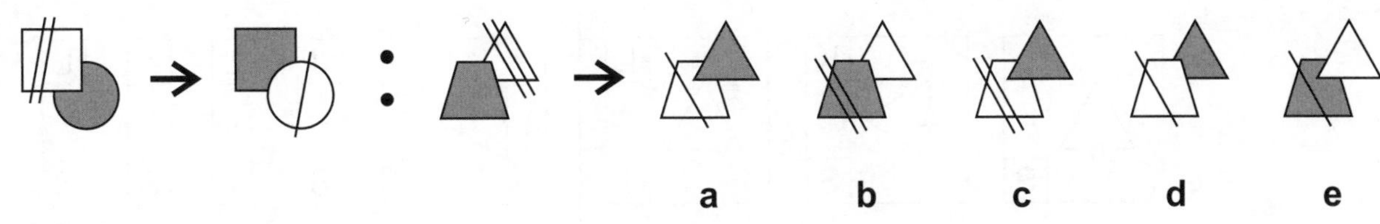

a b c d e

10

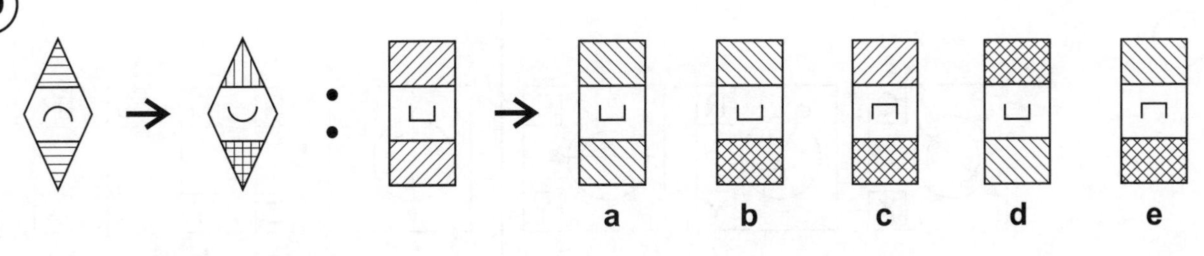

a b c d e

/ 10

Section 2 — Horizontal Code

In the boxes on the left are shapes with code letters. The top letters have a different meaning to the bottom ones. Work out how the letters go with the shapes and then find the code for the new shape from the five codes on the right.

Example:

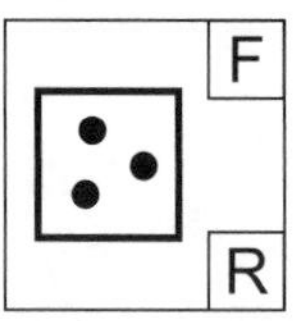

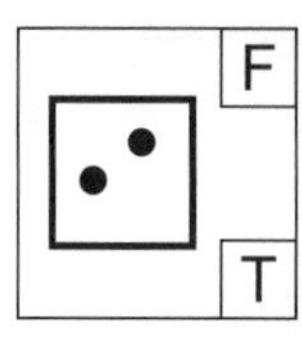

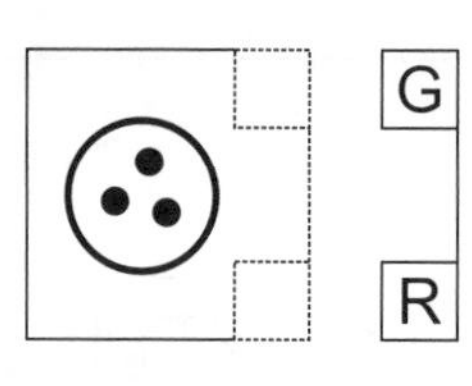

a	b	c	d	e
GR	FT	FR	GT	FG

Answer: a

Both squares have an F at the top, but the circle has a G, so the top code letter must stand for shape. This means that the bottom code letter must be for the number of dots. R is for 3 dots and T is for 2 dots. The new figure must have a G because it is a circle and an R because it has 3 dots. The code must be GR and the answer is a.

Example:

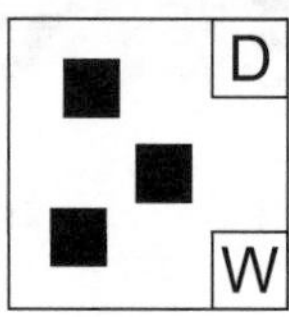

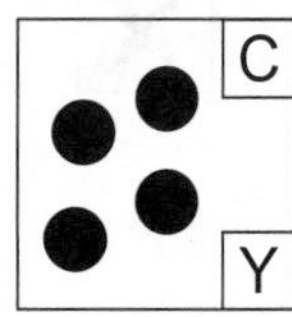

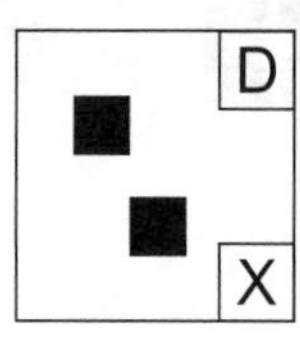

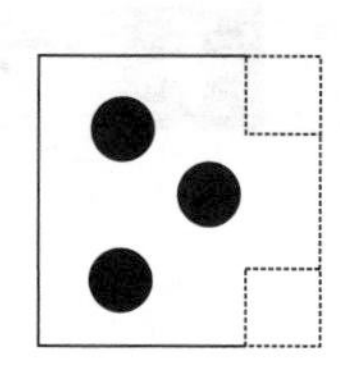
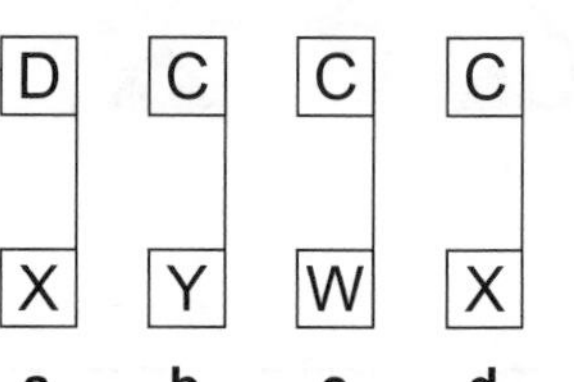

Answer: c

Both figures with squares have a D at the top, and the figure with circles has a C, so the top code letter must be for shape. The bottom code letter must be for the number of shapes. W is for 3 shapes, Y is for 4 and X is for 2. The new figure must have a C because it is made of circles and a W because there are 3 of them. The code must be CW and the answer is c.

1

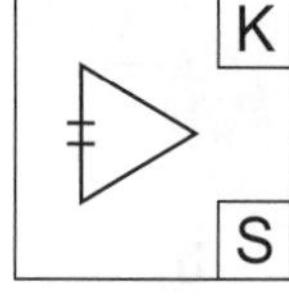

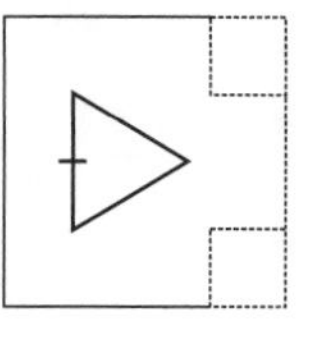
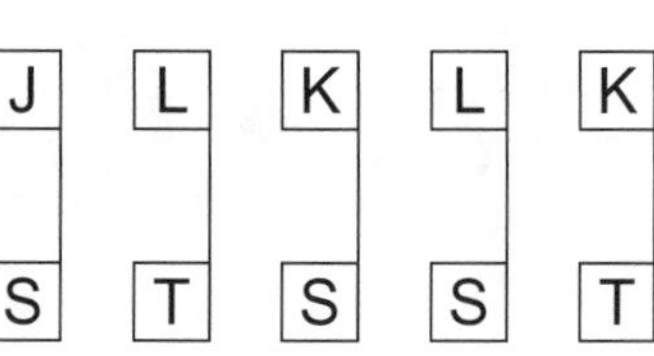

2

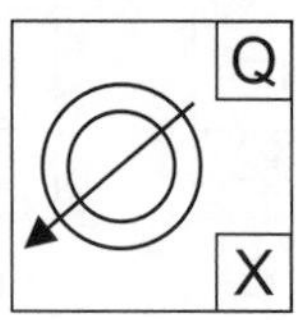

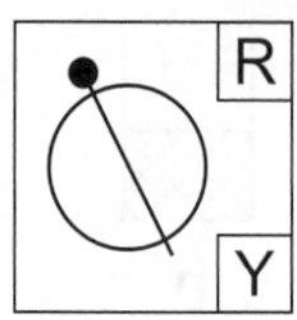

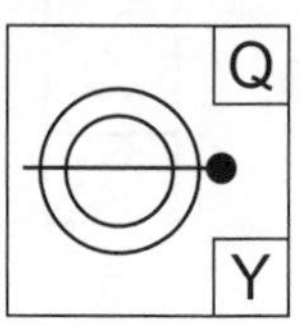

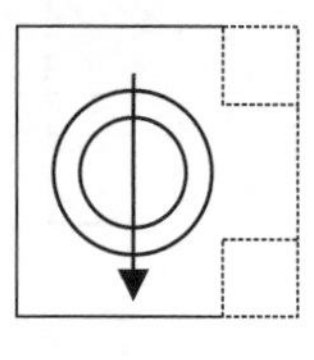
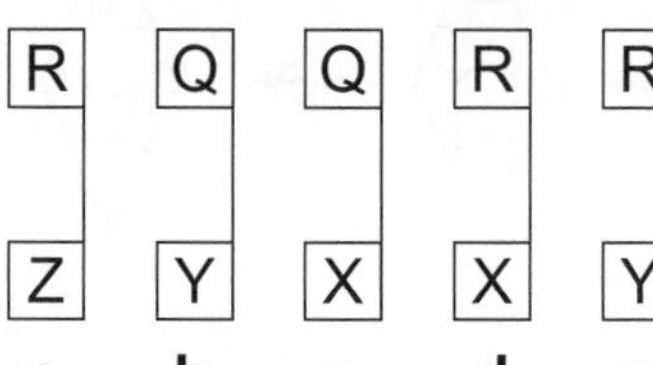

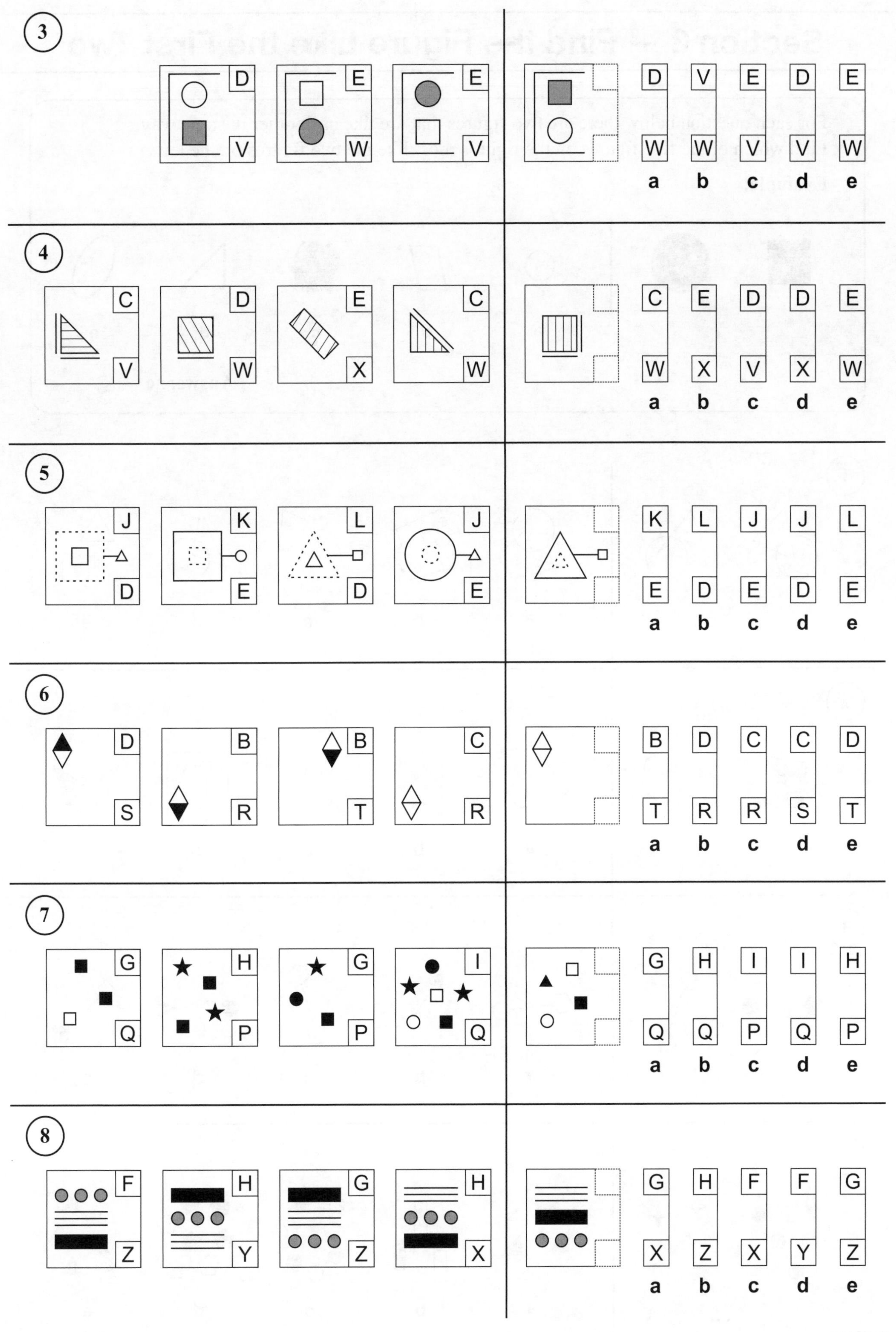
3
D
V
E
W
E
V
D
W
V
W
E
V
D
V
E
W
a
b
c
d
e
4
C
V
D
W
E
X
C
W
C
W
E
X
D
V
D
X
E
W
a
b
c
d
e
5
J
D
K
E
L
D
J
E
K
E
L
D
J
E
J
D
L
E
a
b
c
d
e
6
D
S
B
R
B
T
C
R
B
T
D
R
C
R
C
S
D
T
a
b
c
d
e
7
G
Q
H
P
G
P
I
Q
G
Q
H
Q
I
P
I
Q
H
P
a
b
c
d
e
8
F
Z
H
Y
G
Z
H
X
G
X
H
Z
F
X
F
Y
G
Z
a
b
c
d
e

/ 8

Section 3 — Find the Figure Like the First Two

For each question below there are two figures that are like each other in some way.
Find which of the five figures on the right is most like the two figures on the left.

Example:

  |     

a b c d e

Answer: c

  |  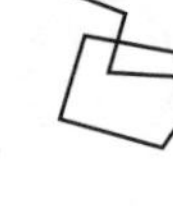   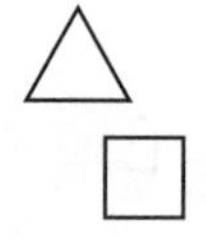

a  c d e

(2)

 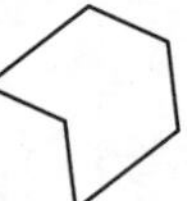 | 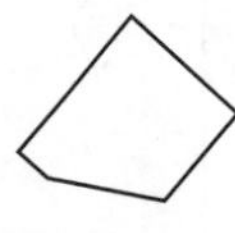  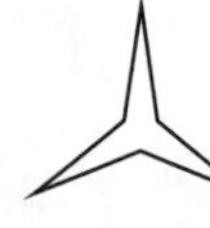  

a b c d e

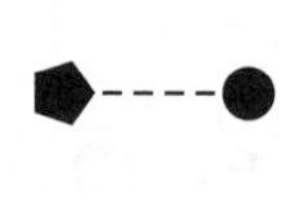 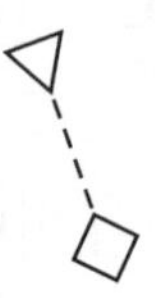 | 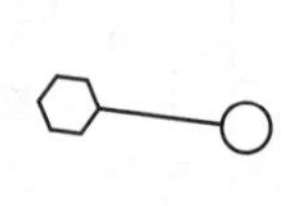 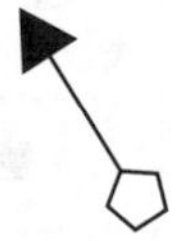 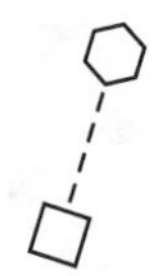 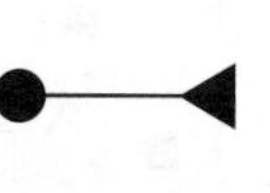

a b c d e

(4)

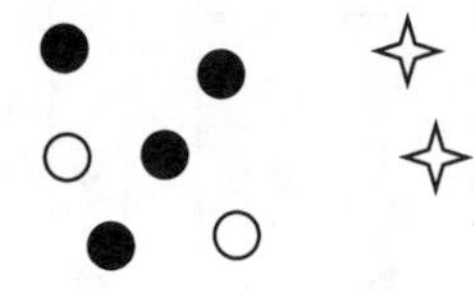 | 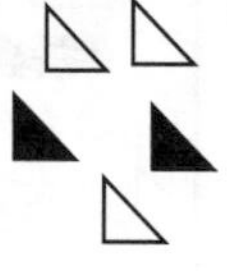 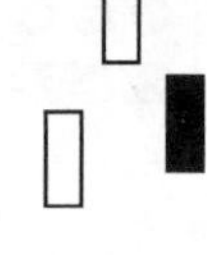 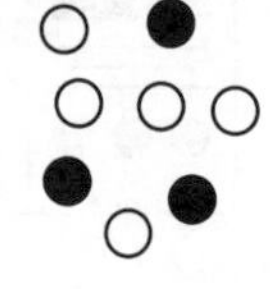 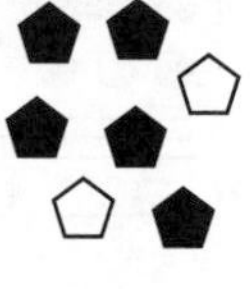 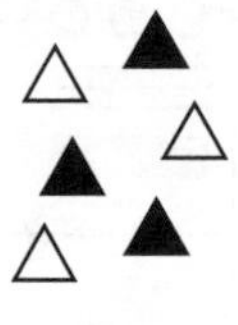

a b c d e

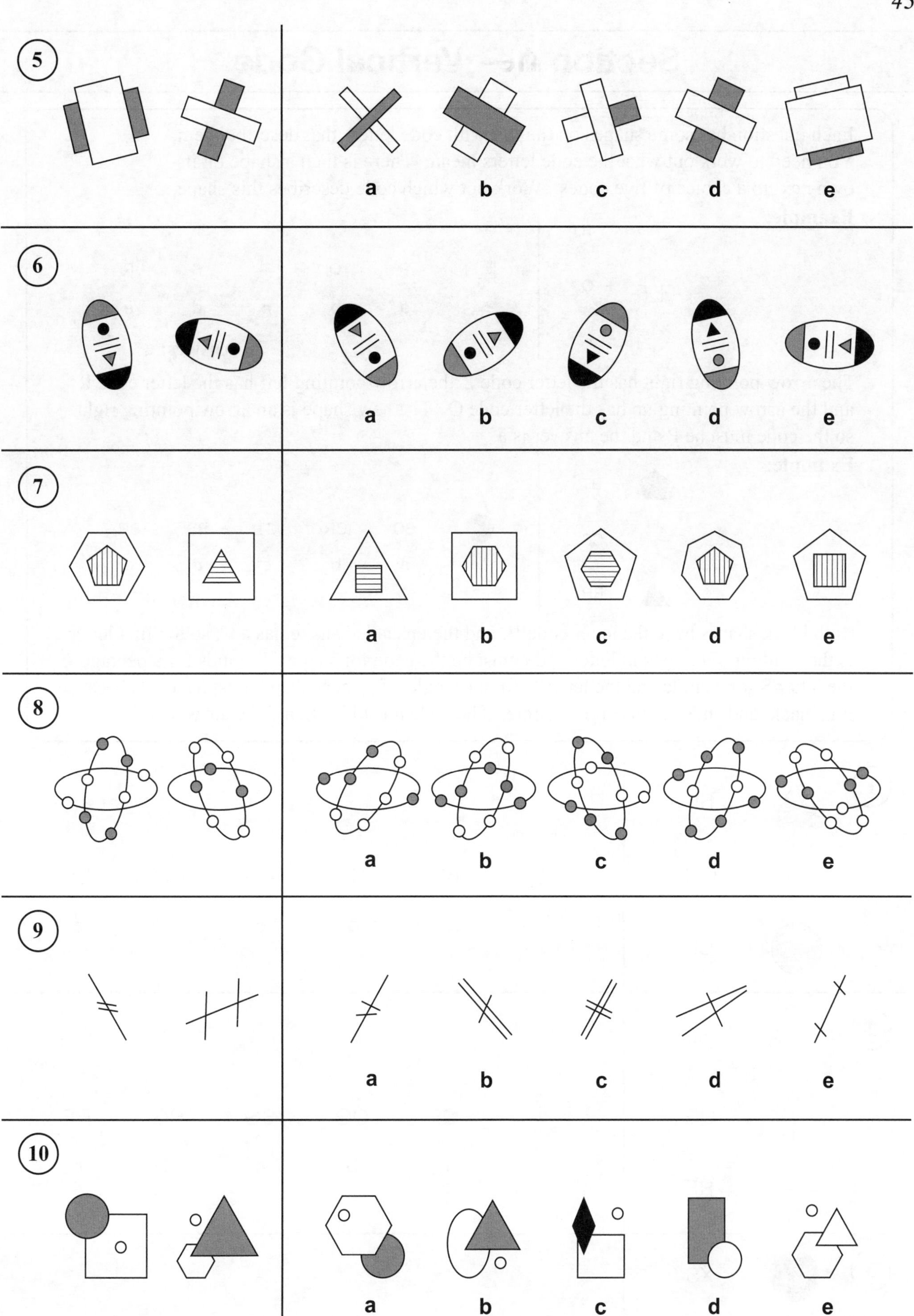

/ 10

Section 4 — Vertical Code

Each question has some shapes on the left with code letters that describe them. You need to work out what the code letters mean. There is then a shape on its own next to a choice of five codes. Work out which code describes this shape.

Example:

P

Q

R

P	Q	T	S	R
a	**b**	**c**	**d**	**e**

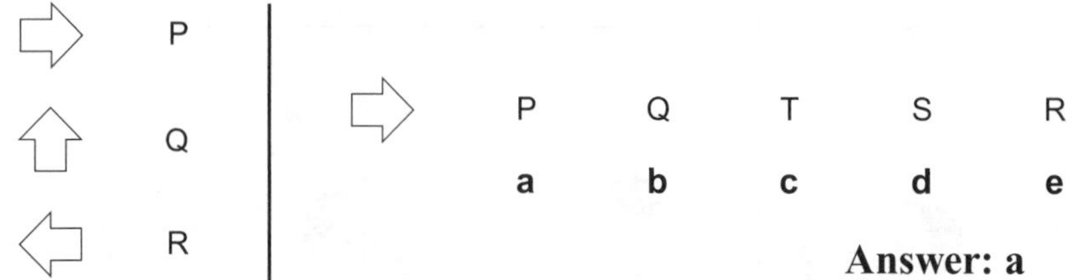

Answer: a

The arrow pointing right has the letter code P, the arrow pointing left has the letter code R, and the arrow pointing up has the letter code Q. The new shape is an arrow pointing right, so the code must be P and the answer is a.

Example:

BT

CS

BR

BC	CR	CT	BS	BR
a	**b**	**c**	**d**	**e**

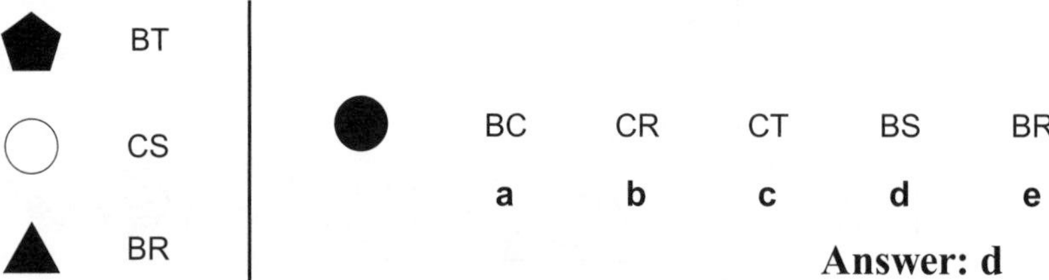

Answer: d

Both black shapes have the letter code B, and the unshaded shape has a C, so the first letter is the shading. The second letter code must be the code for shape. T stands for a pentagon, the letter S for a circle and the letter R for a triangle. The new shape must have a B because it is black, and an S because it is a circle. The code must be BS and the answer is d.

1

BL

CM

CL

BM	CL	AM	CM	BL
a	**b**	**c**	**d**	**e**

2

QF

QG

RF

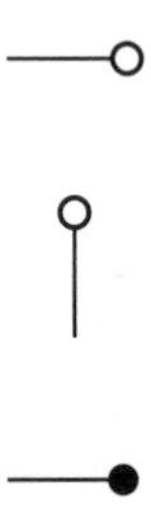

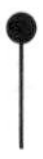

QF	QG	SG	RG	RF
a	**b**	**c**	**d**	**e**

3

XS

YS

ZT

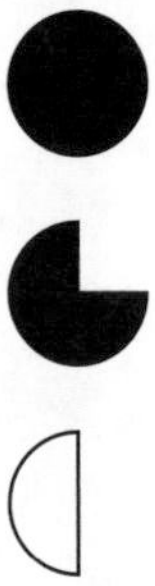

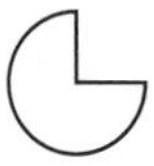

ZS	YT	WS	XT	ZT
a	**b**	**c**	**d**	**e**

4

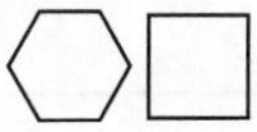	SG
	TG
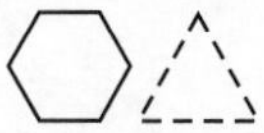	TH
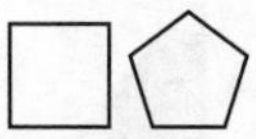	SH

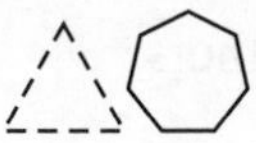

SG TH SH TG RG

a b c d e

5

	CM
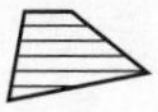	BN
	CN
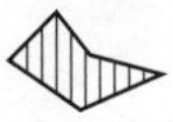	CL

CL DN BL BM CM

a b c d e

6

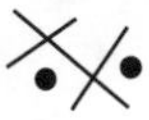	XF
	YG
	XE

XF YE XG ZE YF

a b c d e

7

	PKW
	PJW
	PKX
	QKX

PJX QJW PKX QJX QKW

a b c d e

8

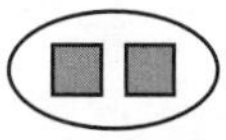	NYC
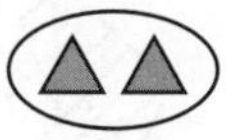	OYC
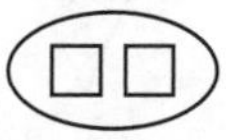	NZC
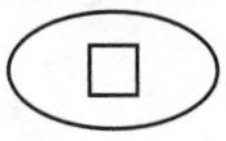	NZD

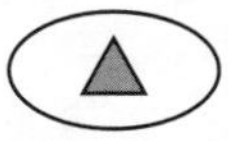

OZC NYD OZD OYD NZC

a b c d e

/ 8

Section 5 — Odd One Out

Each of the questions below has five figures.
Find which figure in each row is most unlike the others.

Example:

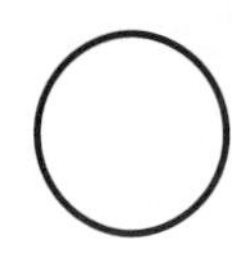

a b c d e

Answer: b

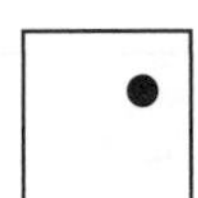

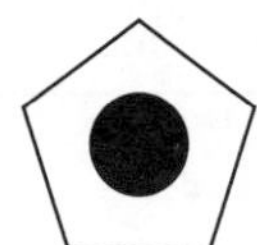

a b c d e

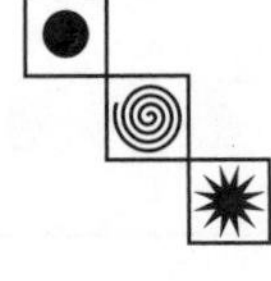

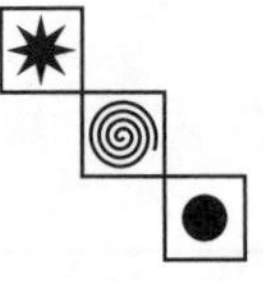
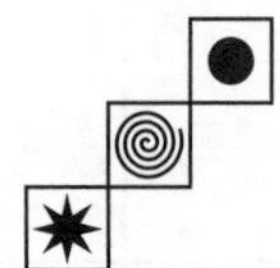

a b c d e

3

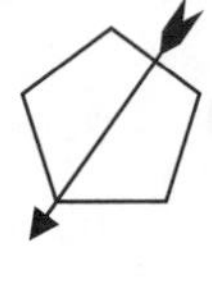

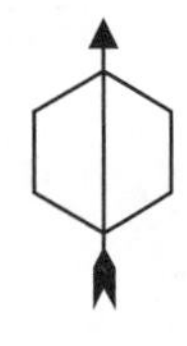
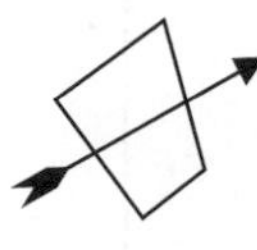
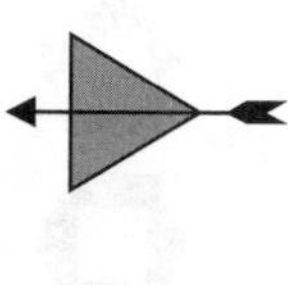

a b c d e

4

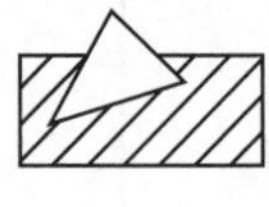

a b c d e

5

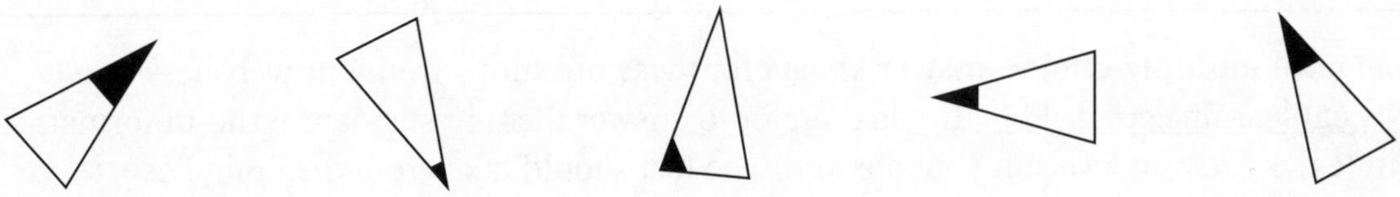

a b c d e

6

a b c d e

7

a b c d e

8

a b c d e

9

a b c d e

10

a b c d e

/ 10 Total / 46

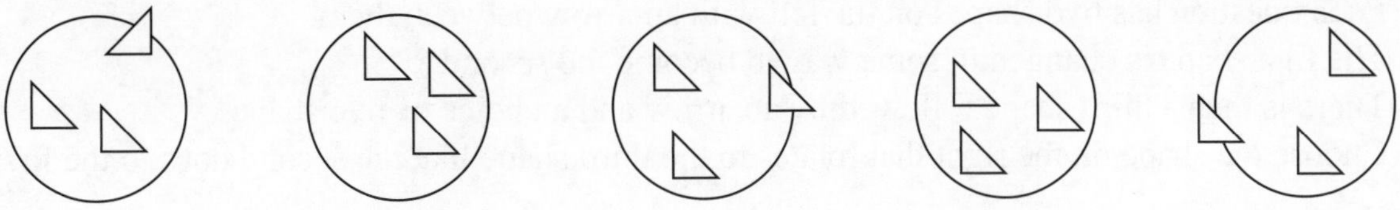

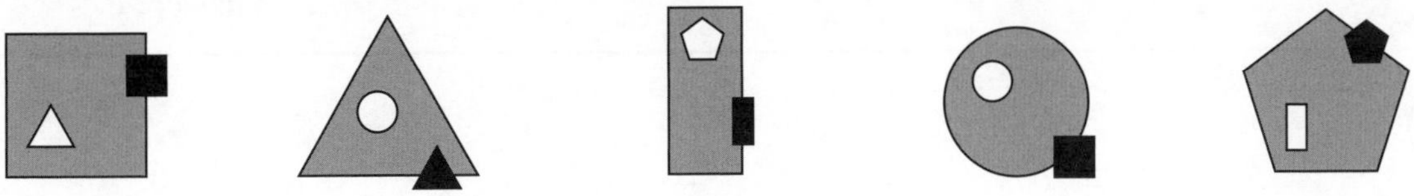

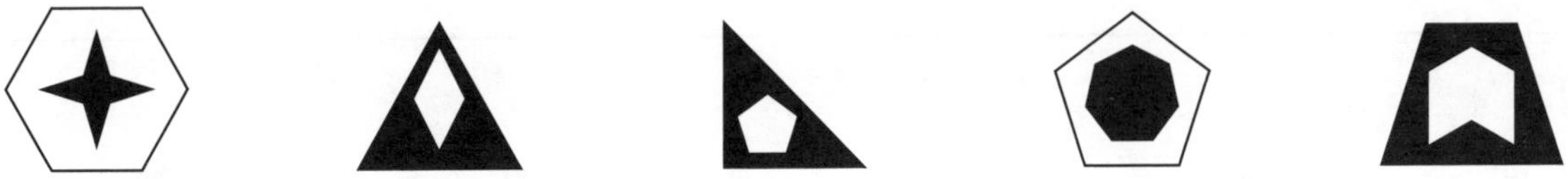

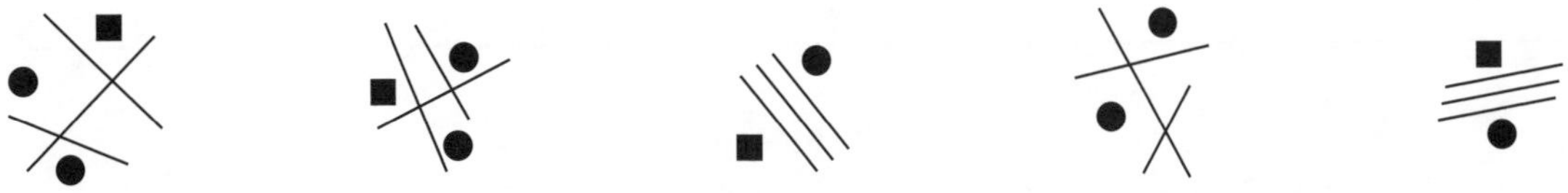

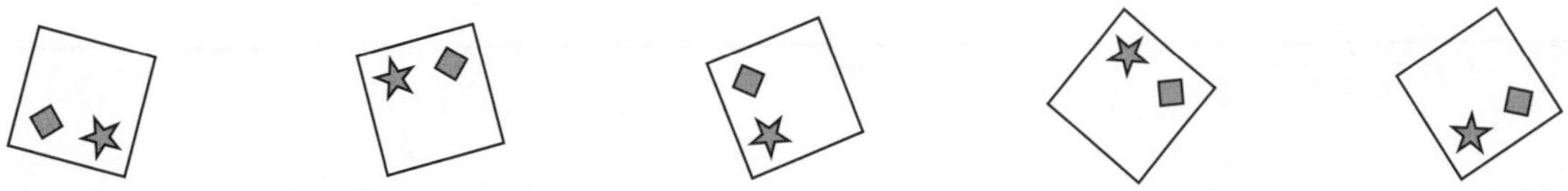

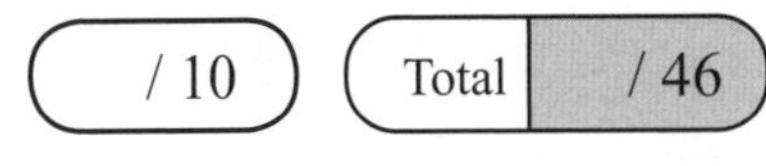

END OF TEST

Assessment Test 4

You can print **multiple-choice answer sheets** for these questions from our website — go to www.cgplearning.co.uk/11+. If you'd prefer to answer them in standard write-in format, just circle the letter underneath your answer. The test should take around 25 minutes.

Section 1 — Complete the Pair

Each question has two shapes on the left with an arrow between them.
The first shape is changed in some way to become the second.
There is then a third shape followed by an arrow and a choice of five shapes.
Choose the shape on the right that relates to the third shape like the second does to the first.

Example:

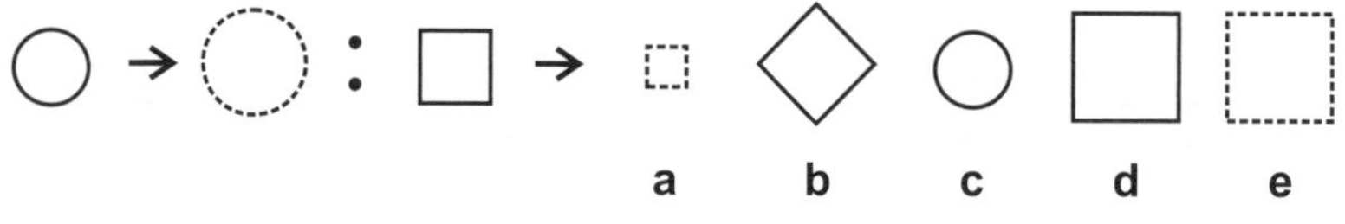

Answer: e

1

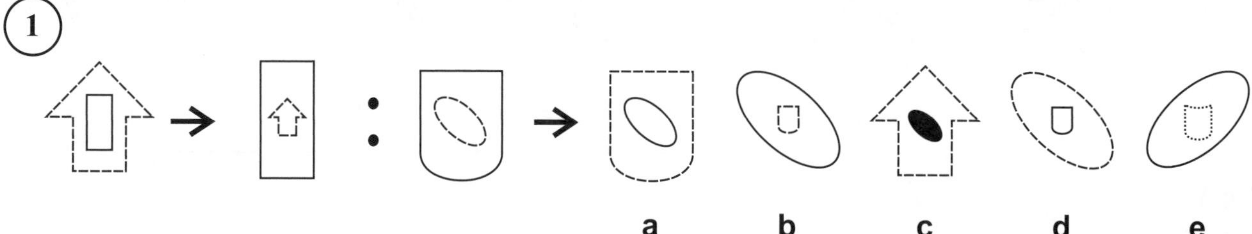

2

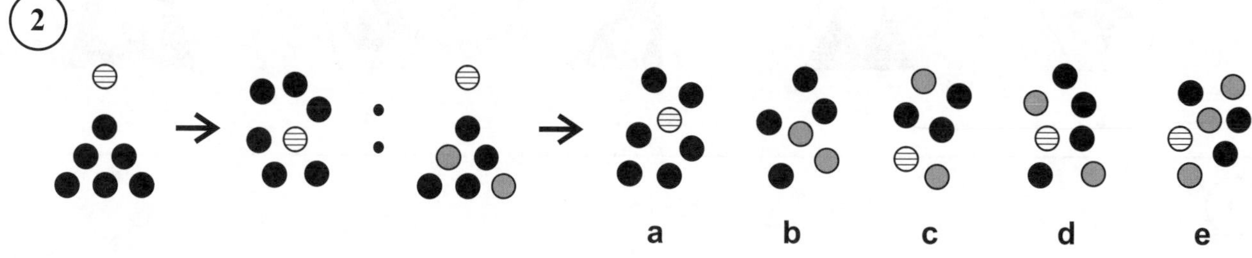

3

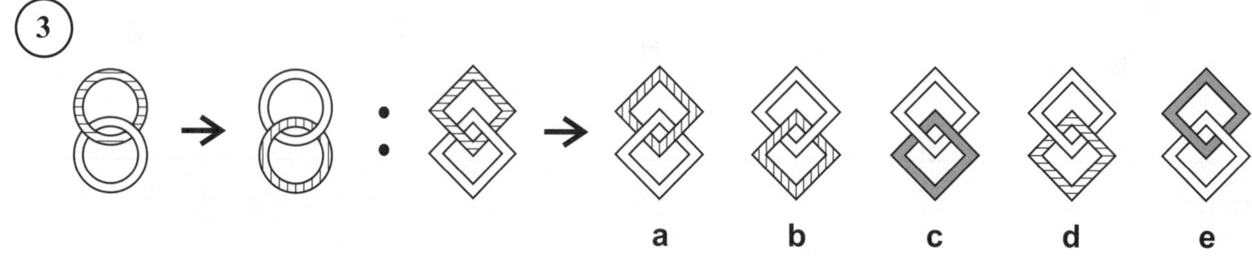

4

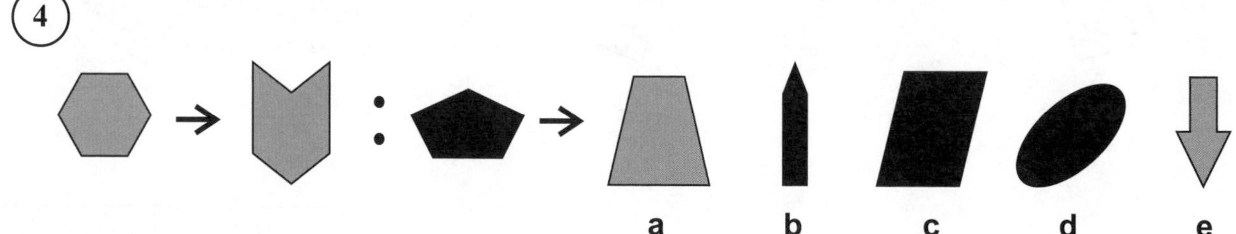

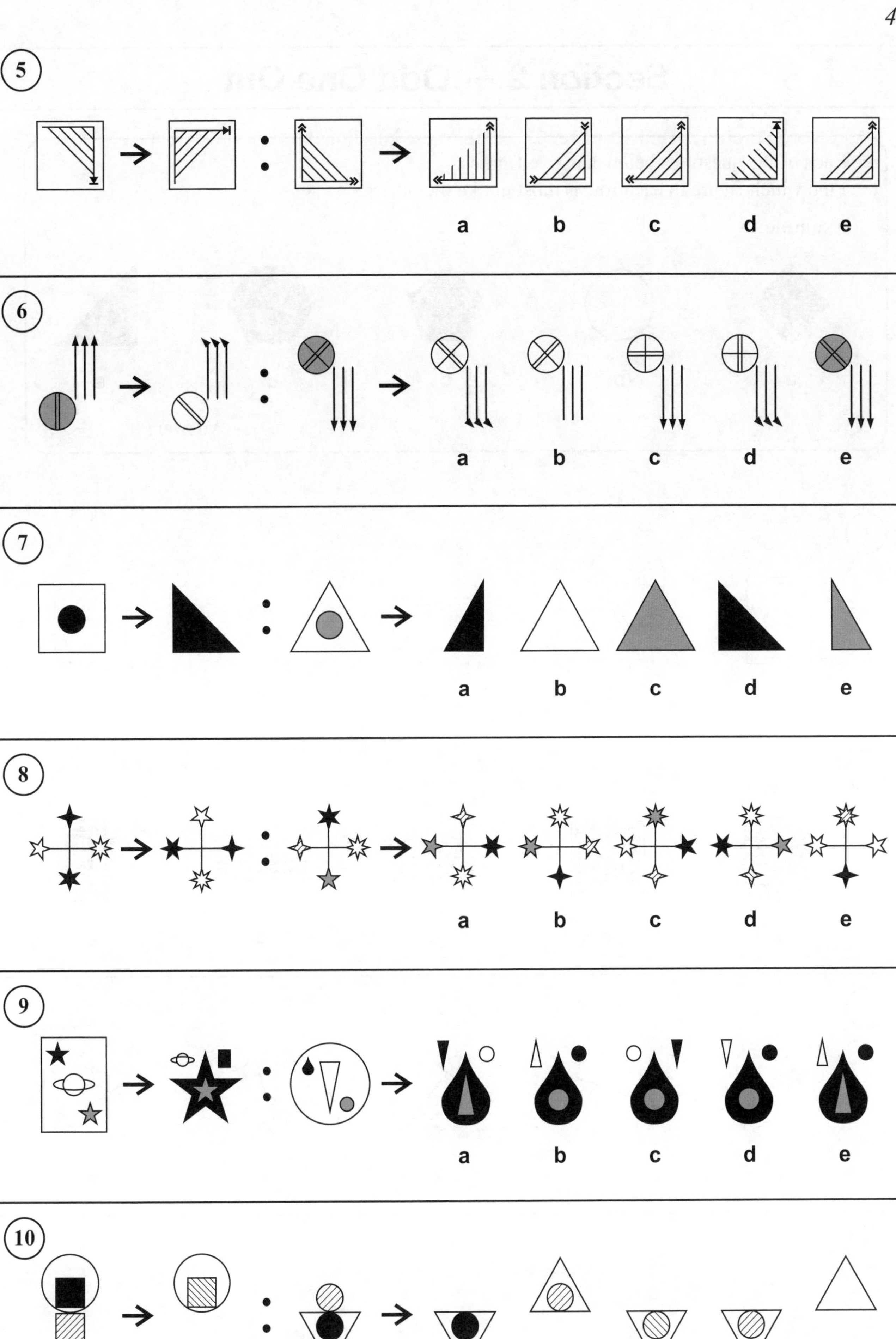

/ 10

Section 2 — Odd One Out

Each of the questions below has five figures.
Find which figure in each row is most unlike the others.

Example:

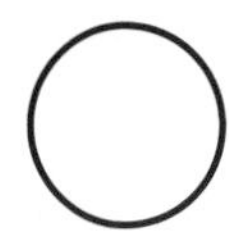

a b c d e

Answer: b

(1)

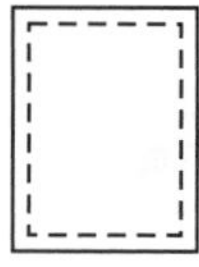

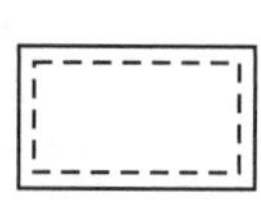

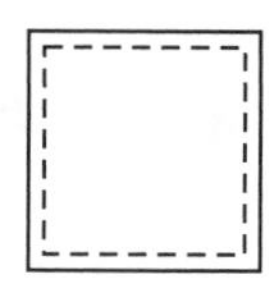

a b c d e

(2)

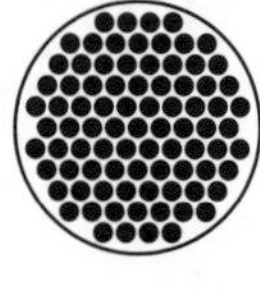
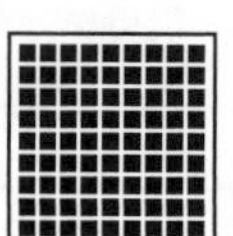
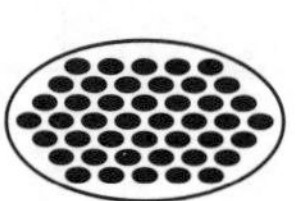

a b c d e

(3)

a b c d e

(4)

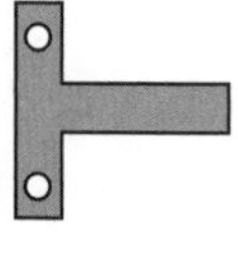
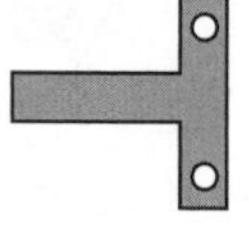
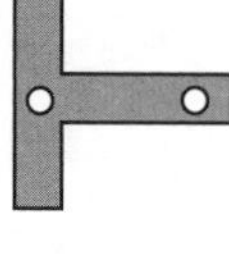
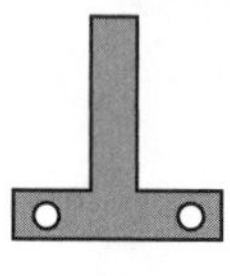

a b c d e

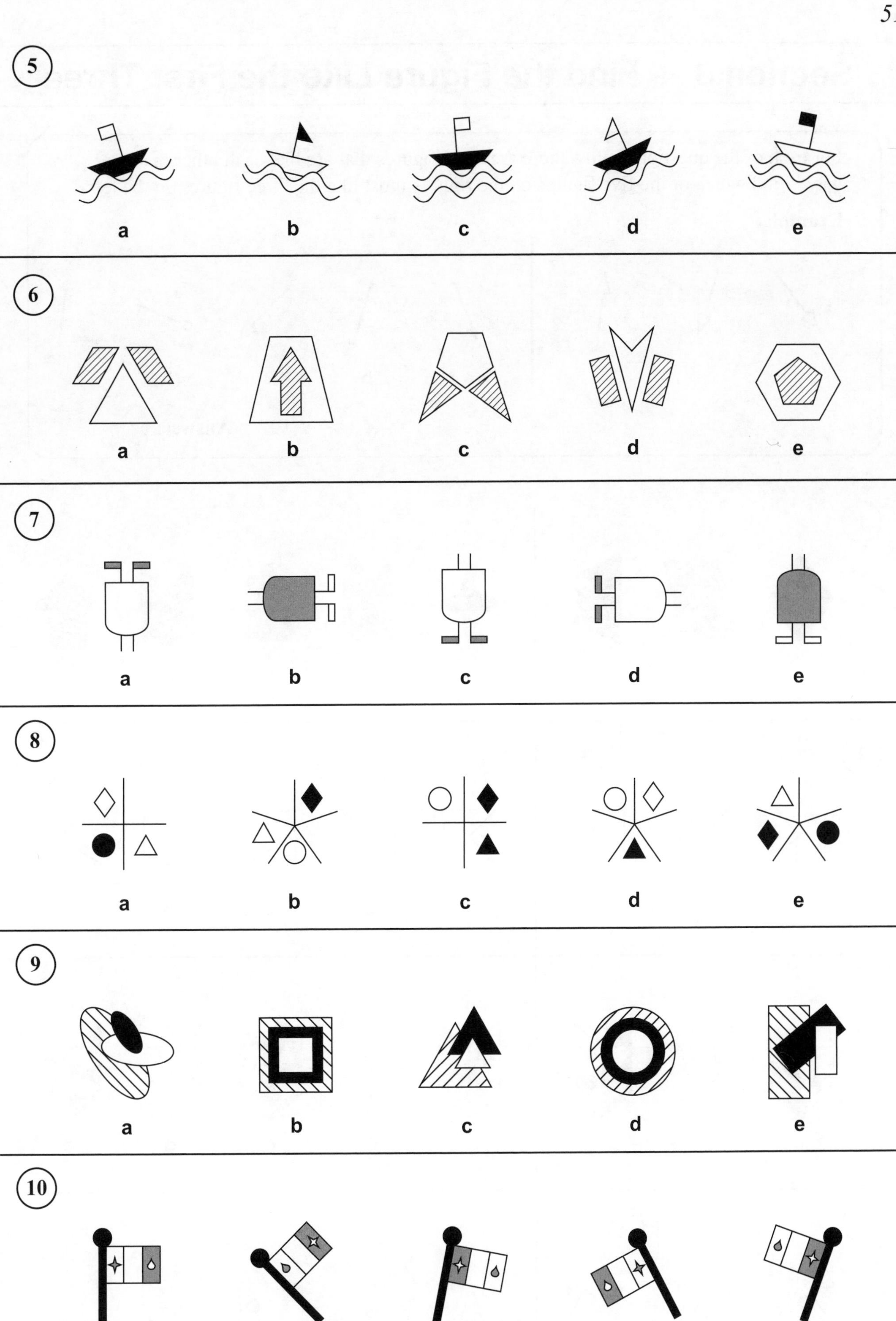

/ 10

Section 3 — Find the Figure Like the First Three

For each of the questions below there are three figures that are like each other in some way. Find which of the five figures on the right is most like the three figures on the left.

Example:

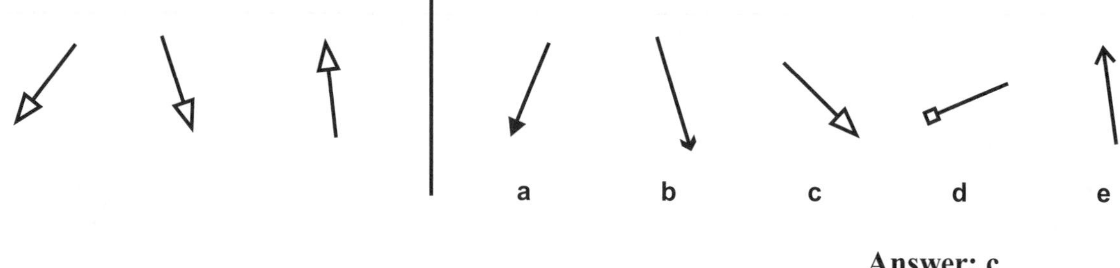

Answer: c

1

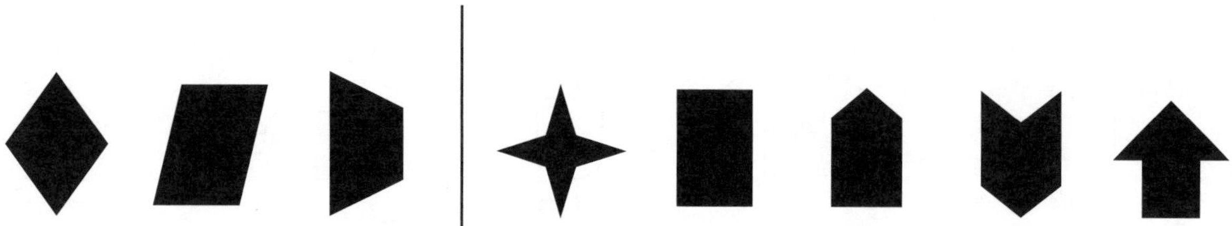

a b c d e

2

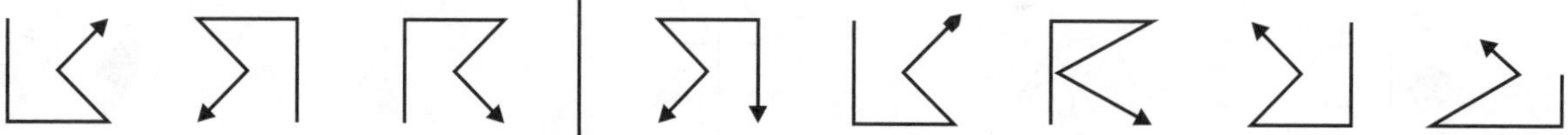

a b c d e

3

a b c d e

4

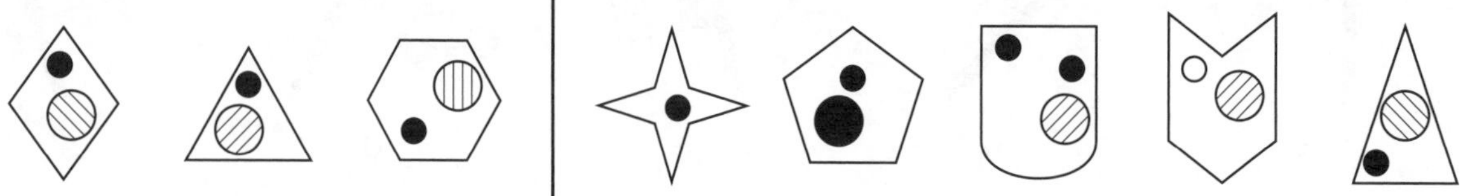

a b c d e

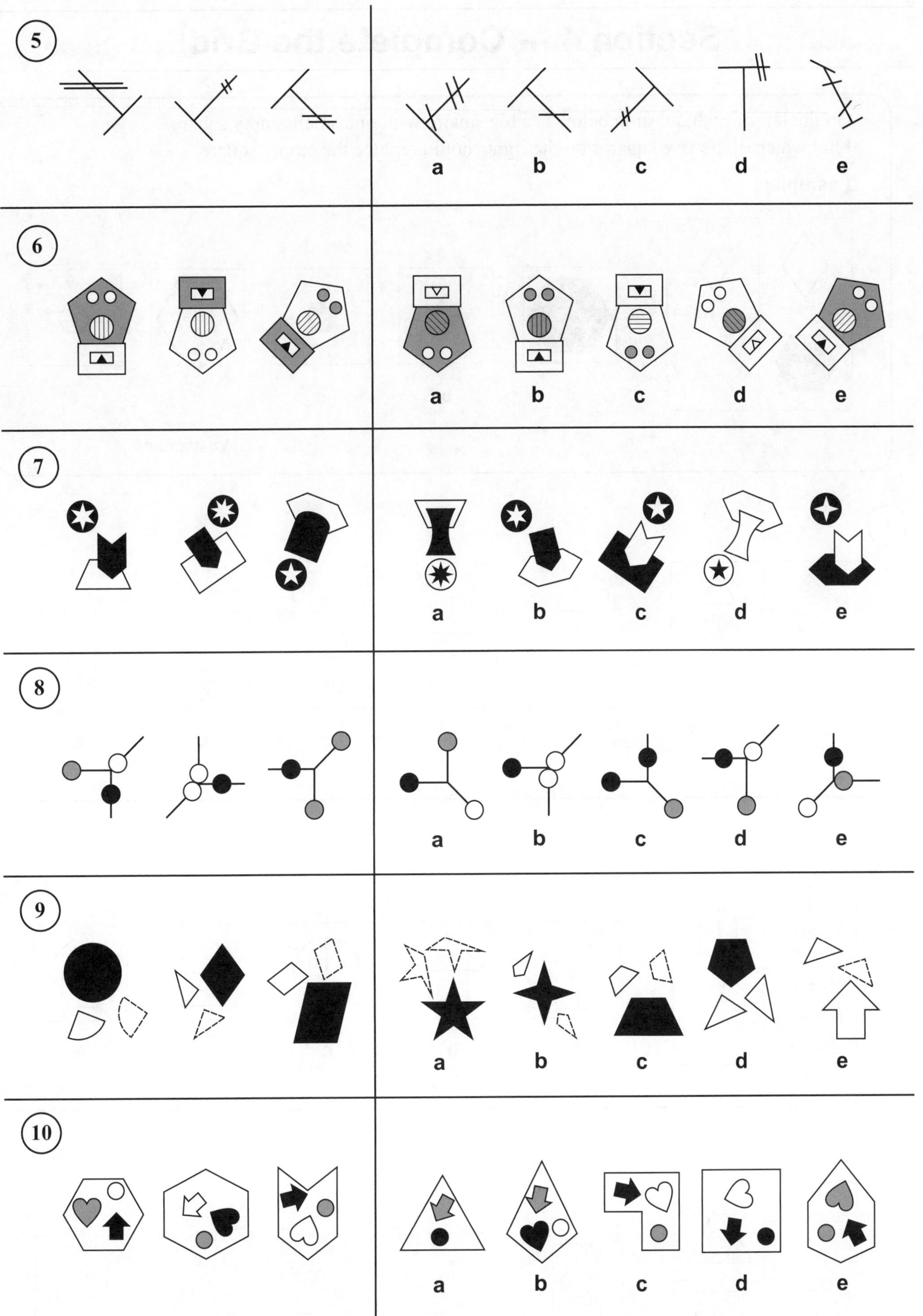

/ 10

Section 4 — Complete the Grid

On the left of each question below is a big square with one small empty square.
Find which of the five squares on the right should replace the empty square.

Example:

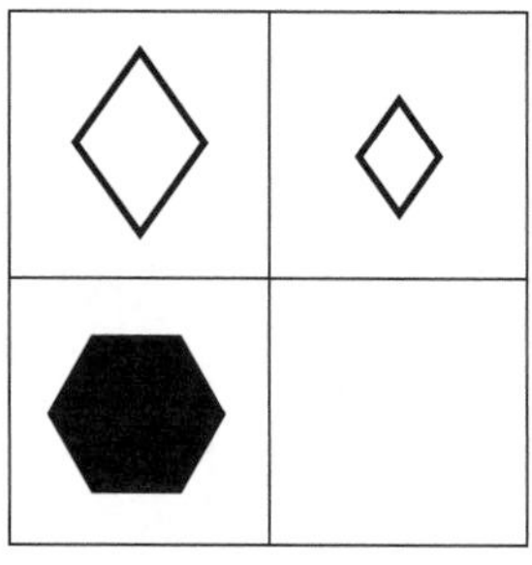

a

b

c

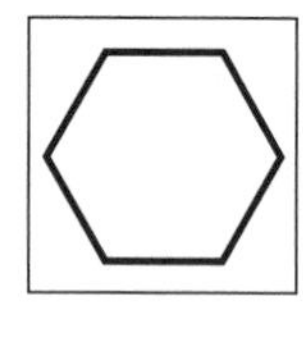
d

e

Answer: c

1

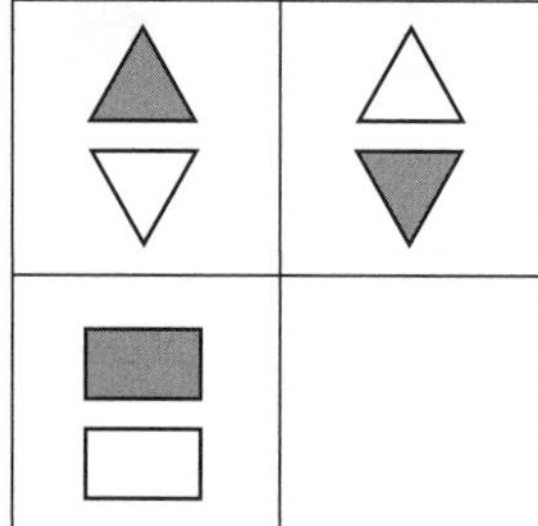

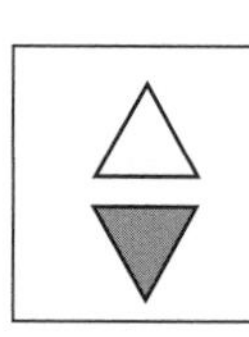
a

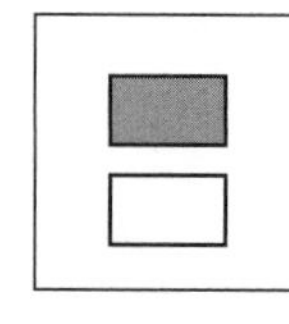
b

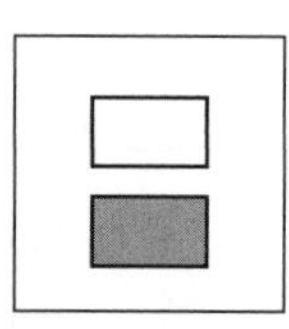
c

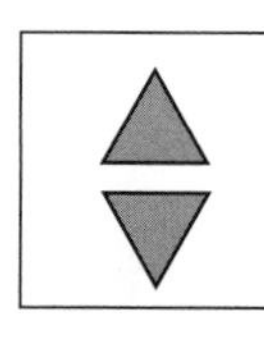
d

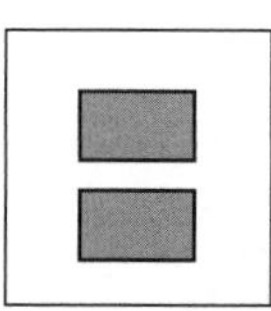
e

2

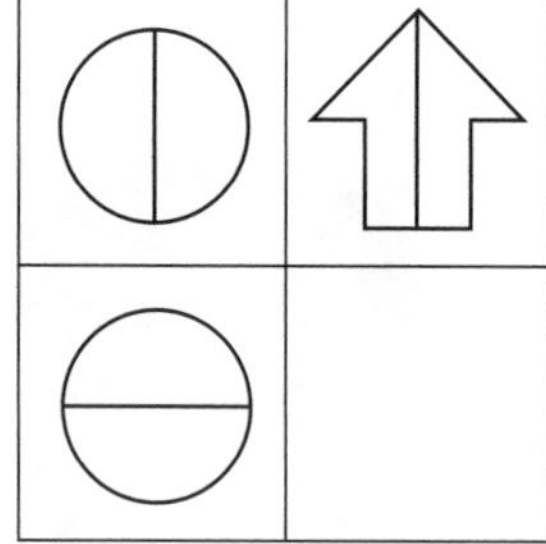

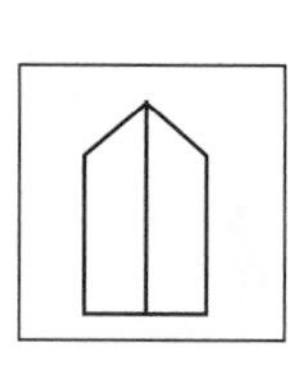
a

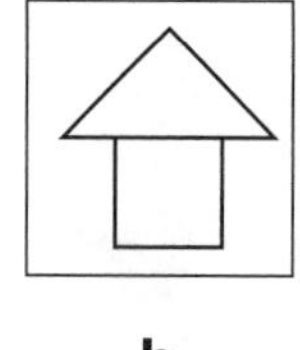
b

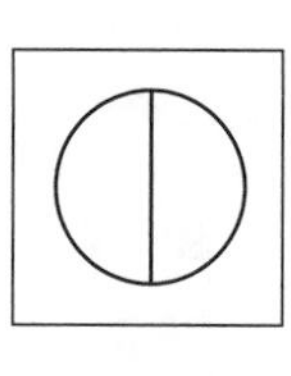
c

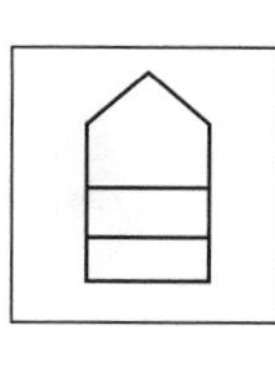
d

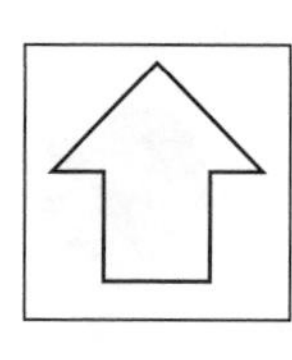
e

3

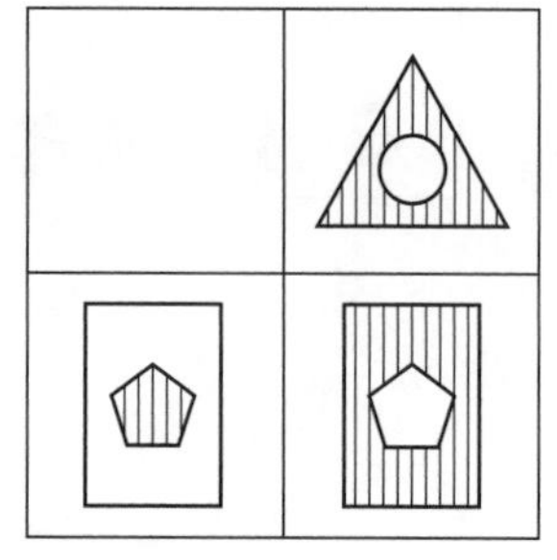

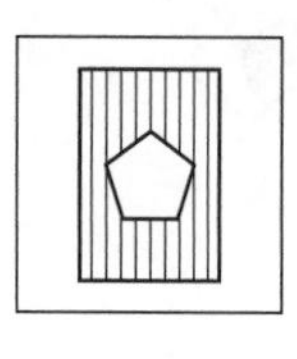
a

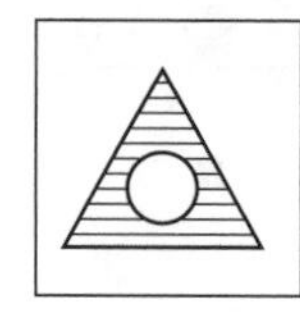
b

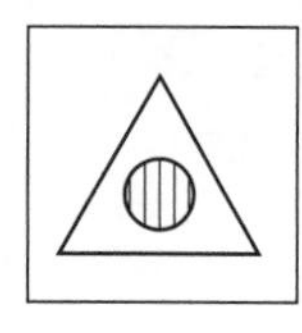
c

d

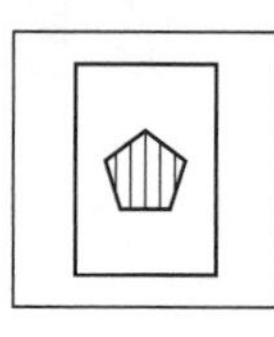
e

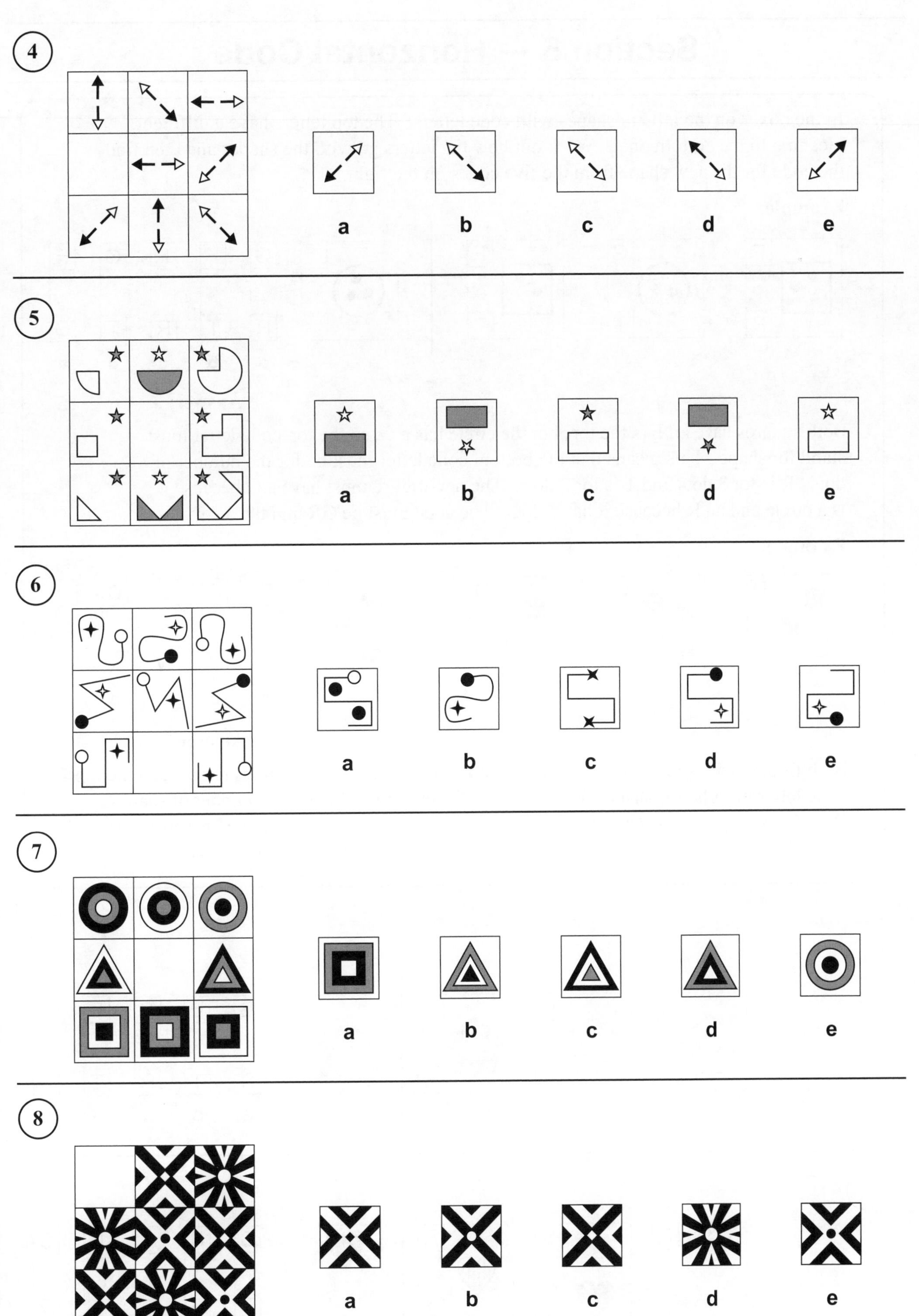

/ 8

Section 5 — Horizontal Code

In the boxes on the left are shapes with code letters. The top letters have a different meaning to the bottom ones. Work out how the letters go with the shapes and then find the code for the new shape from the five codes on the right.

Example:

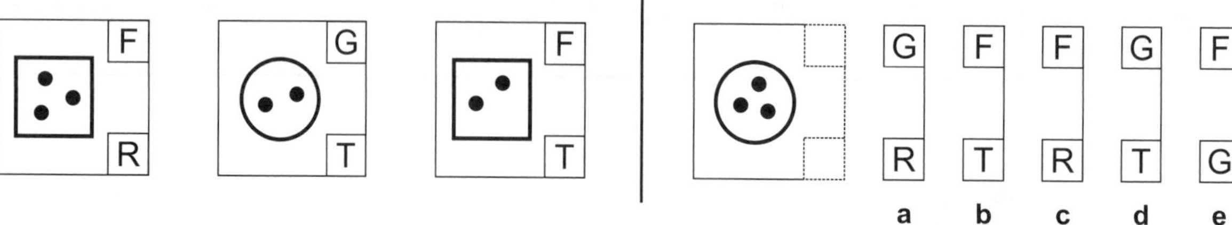

Answer: a

Both squares have an F at the top, but the circle has a G, so the top code letter must stand for shape. This means that the bottom code letter must be for the number of dots. R is for 3 dots and T is for 2 dots. The new figure must have a G because it is a circle and an R because it has 3 dots. The code must be GR and the answer is a.

Example:

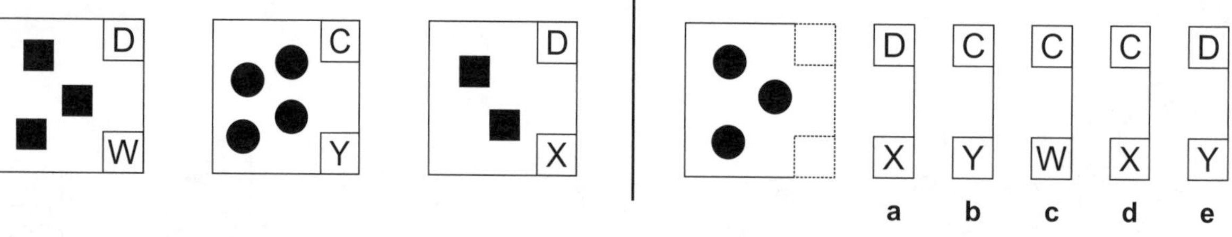

Answer: c

Both figures with squares have a D at the top, and the figure with circles has a C, so the top code letter must be for shape. The bottom code letter must be for the number of shapes. W is for 3 shapes, Y is for 4 and X is for 2. The new figure must have a C because it is made of circles and a W because there are 3 of them. The code must be CW and the answer is c.

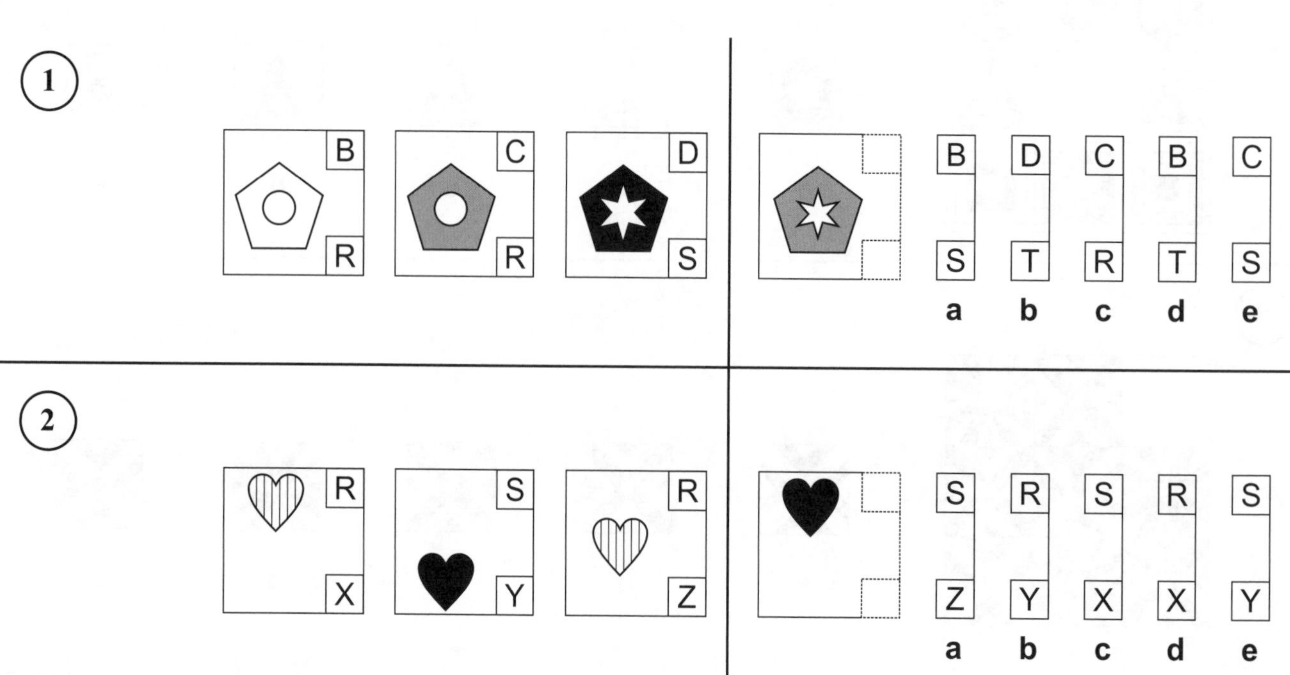

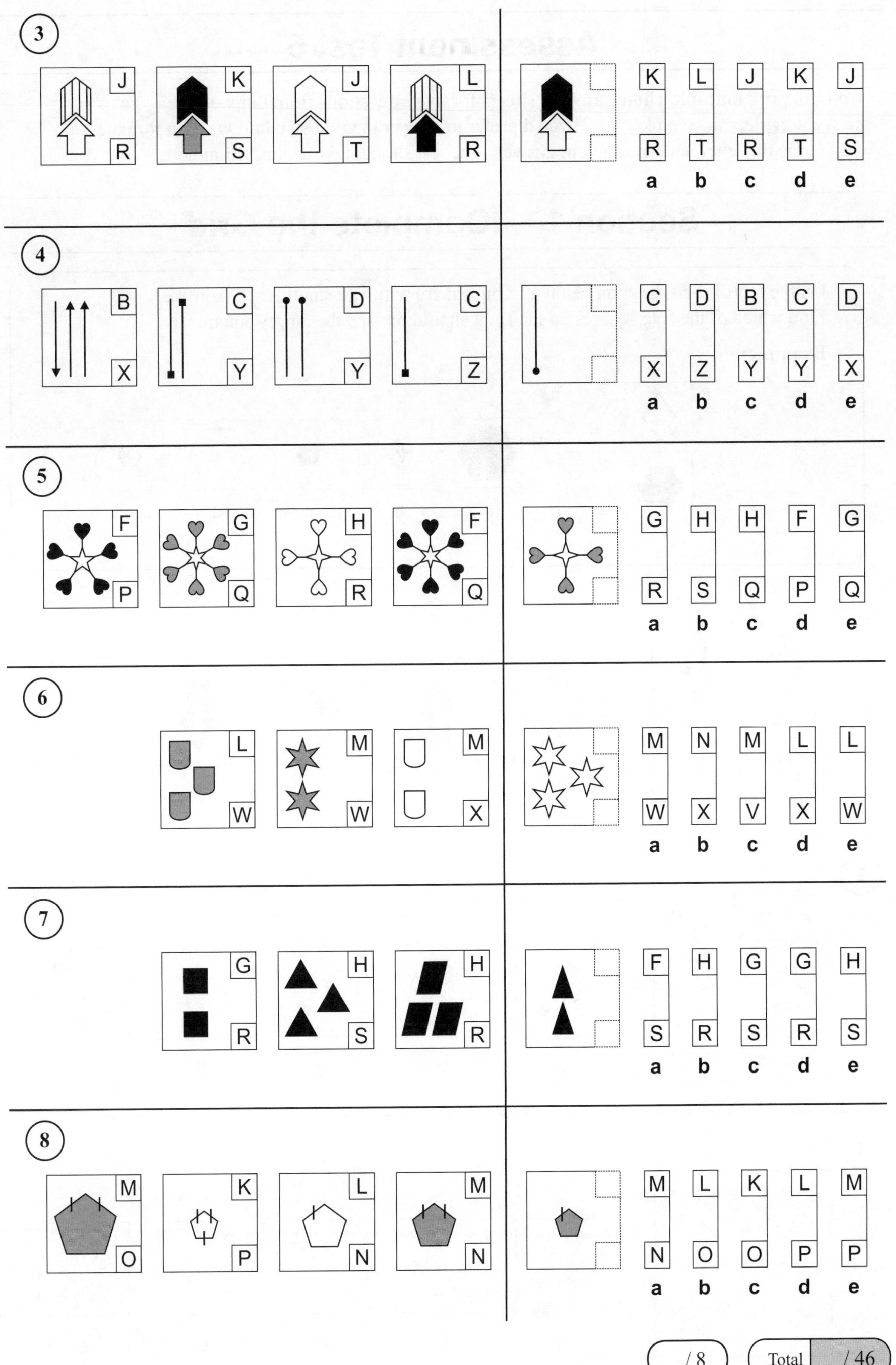
3
J R K S J T L R
K R L T J R K T J S
a b c d e
4
B X C Y D Y C Z
C X D Z B Y C Y D X
a b c d e
5
F P G Q H R F Q
G R H S H Q F P G Q
a b c d e
6
L W M W M X
M W N X M V L X L W
a b c d e
7
G R H S H R
F S H R G S G R H S
a b c d e
8
M O K P L N M N
M N L O K O L P M P
a b c d e

/ 8

Total / 46

Assessment Test 5

You can print **multiple-choice answer sheets** for these questions from our website — go to www.cgplearning.co.uk/11+. If you'd prefer to answer them in standard write-in format, just circle the letter underneath your answer. The test should take around 25 minutes.

Section 1 — Complete the Grid

On the left of each question below is a big square with one small empty square. Find which of the five squares on the right should replace the empty square.

Example:

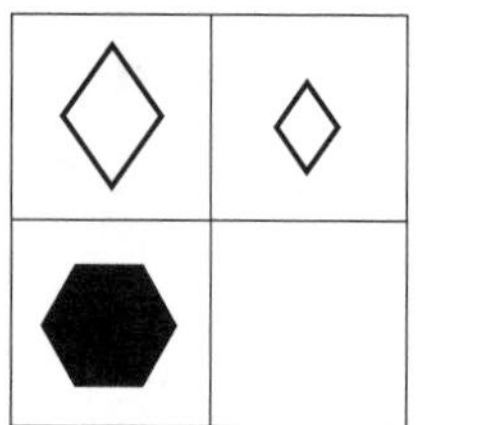

a

b

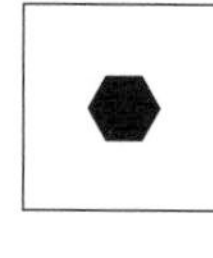
c

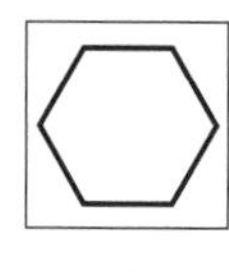
d

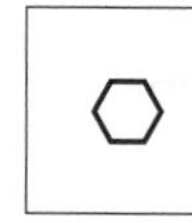
e

Answer: c

1.

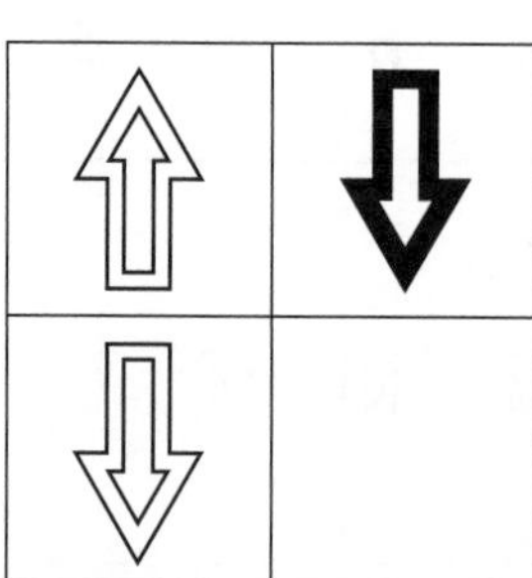

a

b

c

d

e

2.

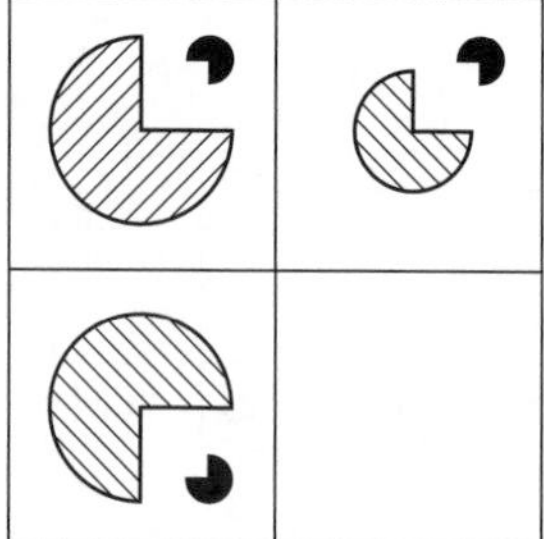

a

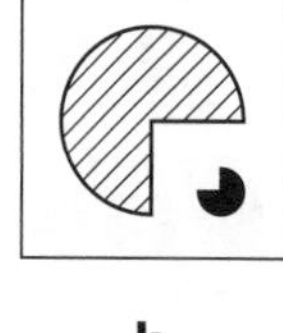
b

c

d

e

3.

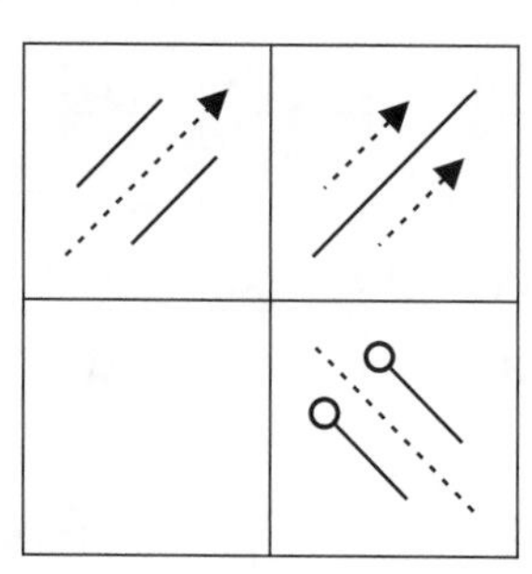

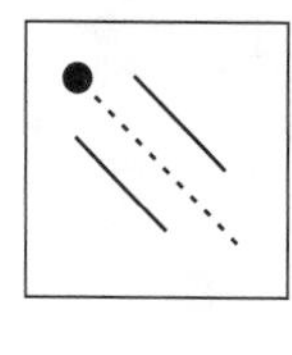
a

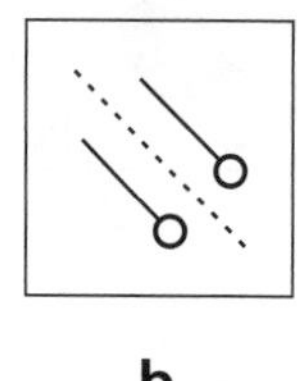
b

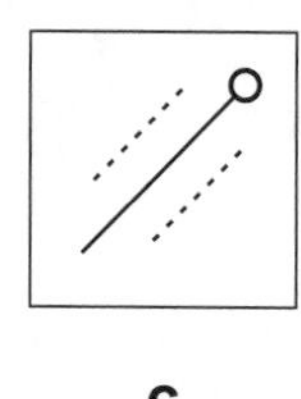
c

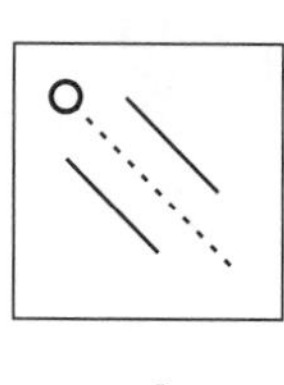
d

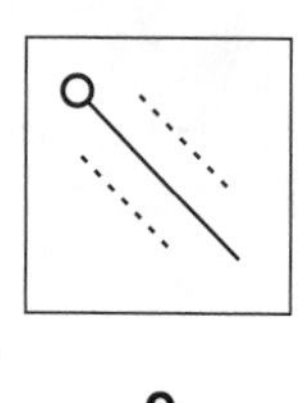
e

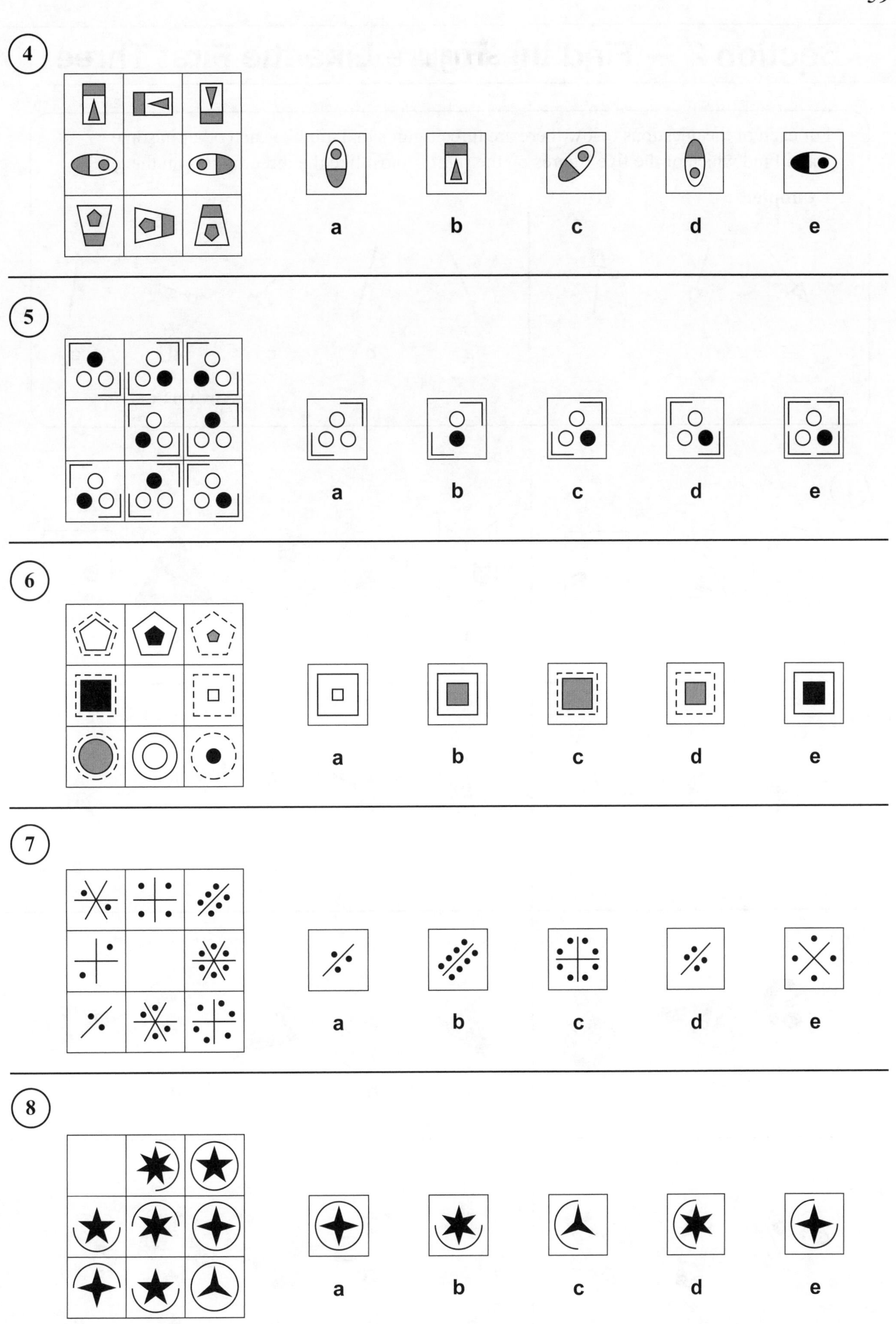

/ 8

Section 2 — Find the Figure Like the First Three

For each of the questions below there are three figures that are like each other in some way. Find which of the five figures on the right is most like the three figures on the left.

Example:

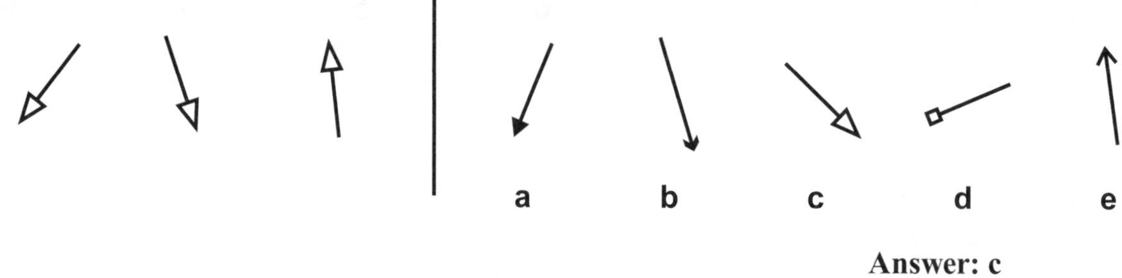

a b c d e

Answer: c

1

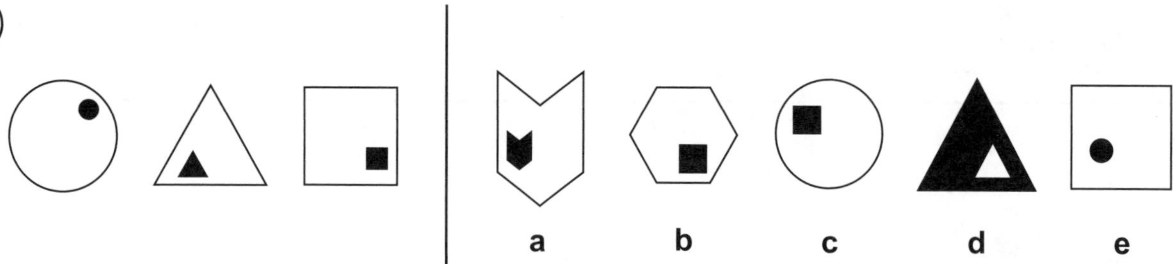

a b c d e

2

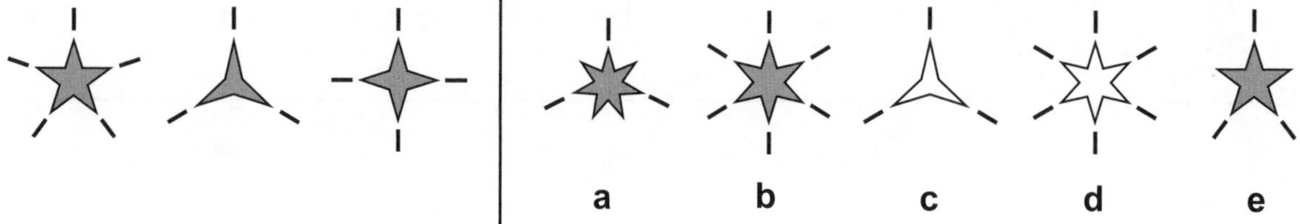

a b c d e

3

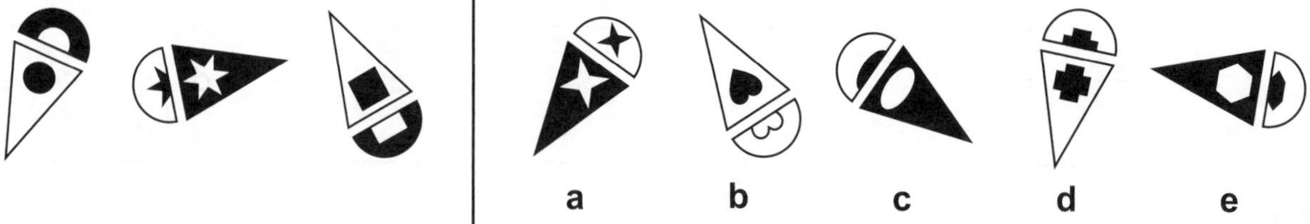

a b c d e

4

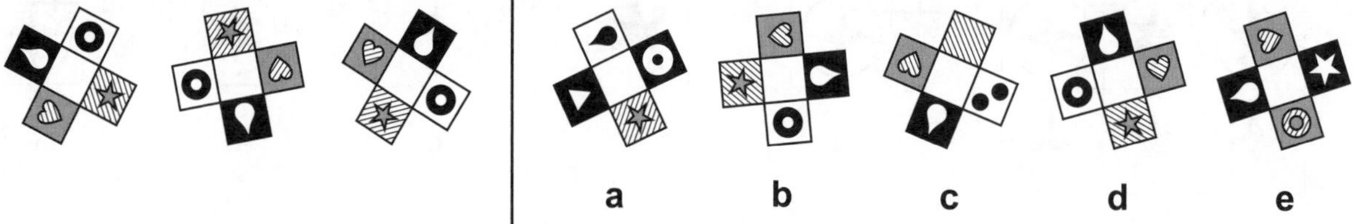

a b c d e

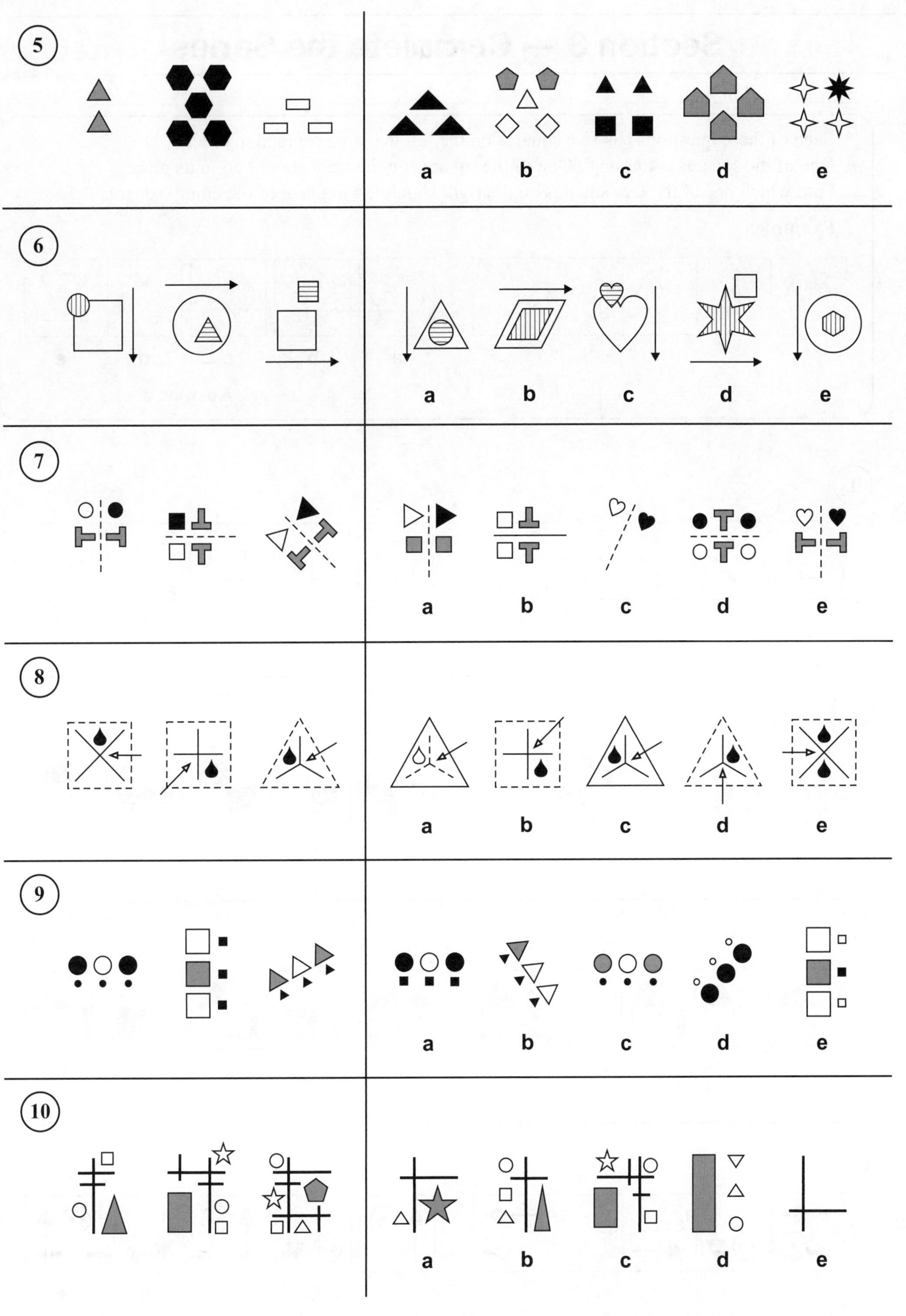

/ 10

Section 3 — Complete the Series

Each of these questions has five squares on the left that are arranged in order.
One of the squares is missing. One of the squares on the right should go in its place.
Find which one of the five squares on the right should go in place of the empty square.

Example:

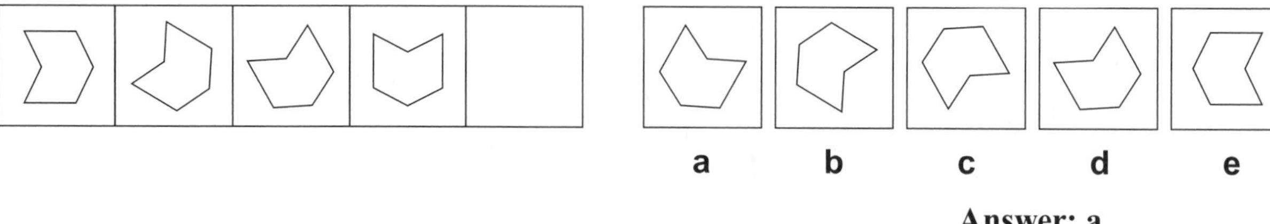

Answer: a

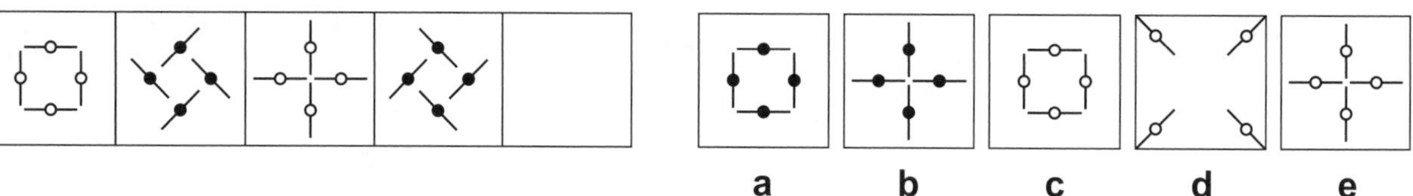

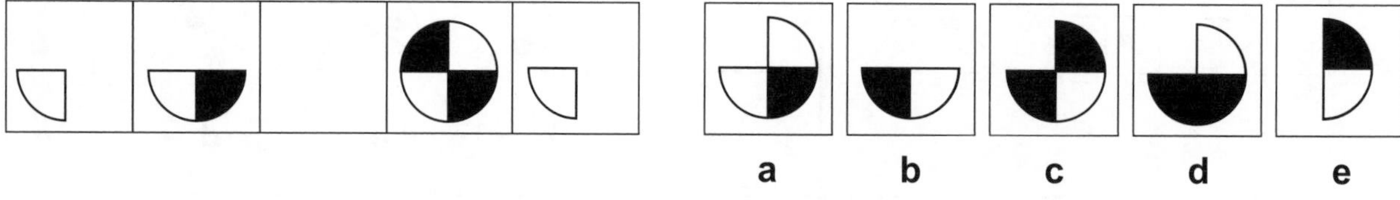

3

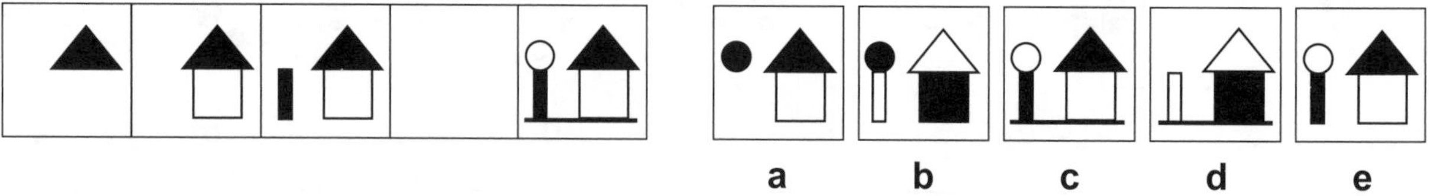

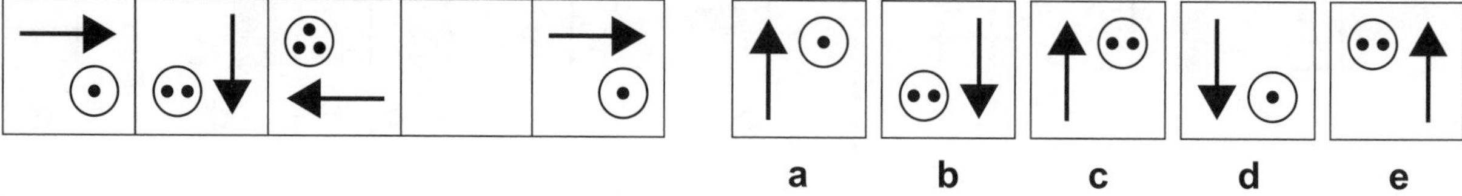

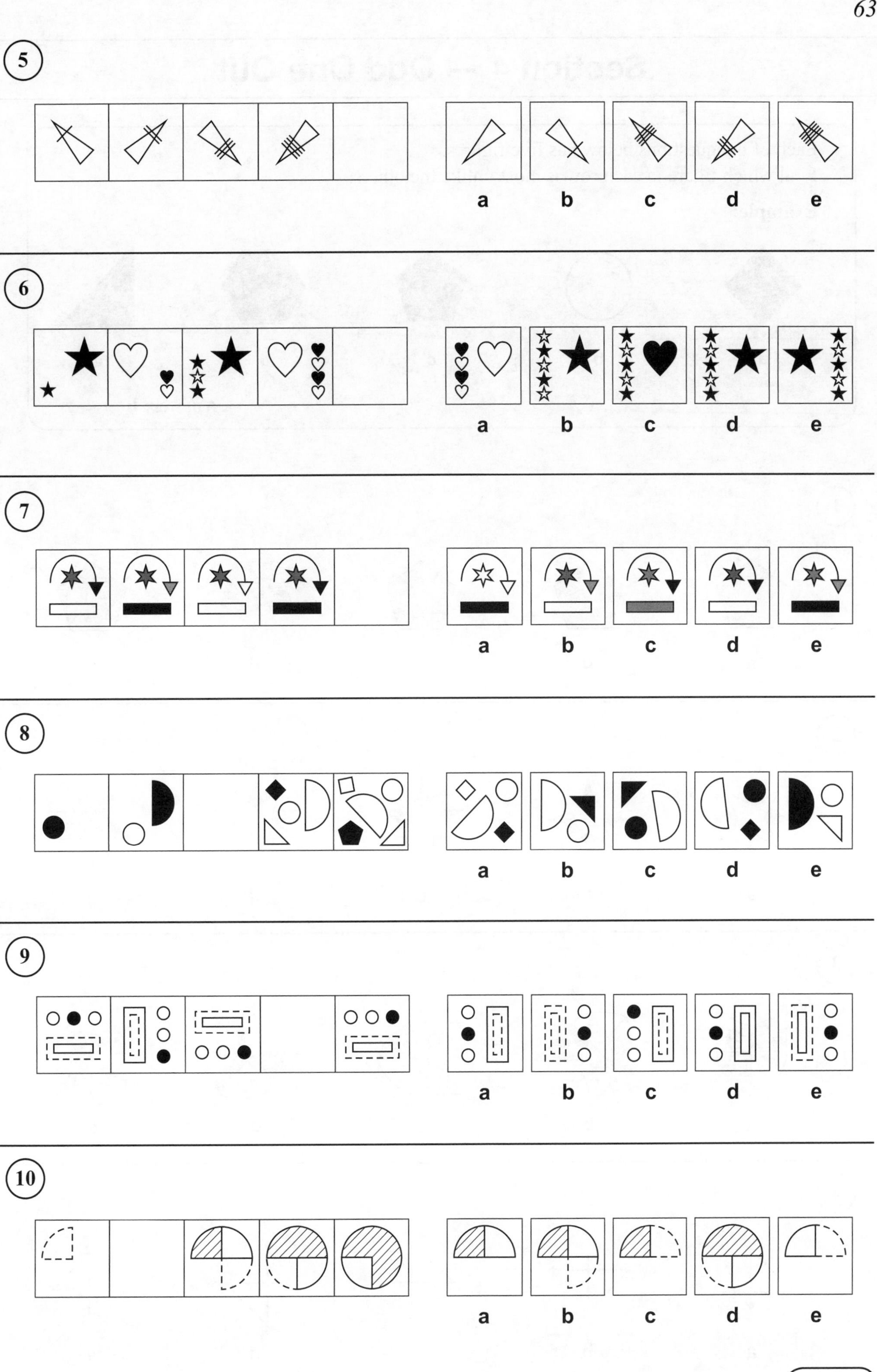

/ 10

Section 4 — Odd One Out

Each of the questions below has five figures.
Find which figure in each row is most unlike the others.

Example:

a

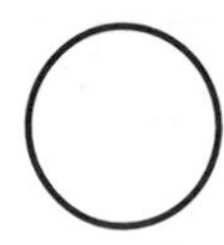
b

c

d

e

Answer: b

1

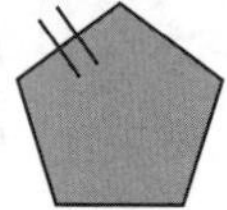
a

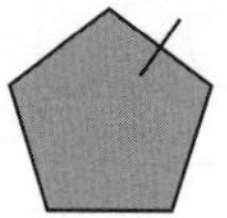
b

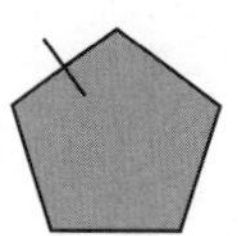
c

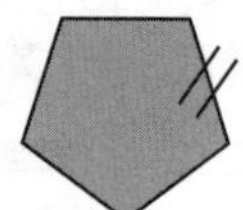
d

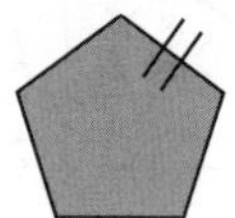
e

2

a

b

c

d

e

3

a

b

c

d

e

4

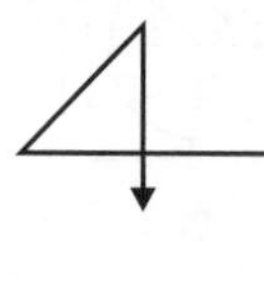
a

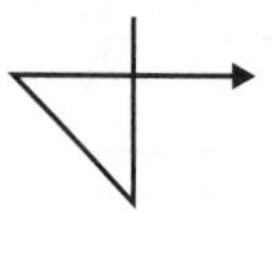
b

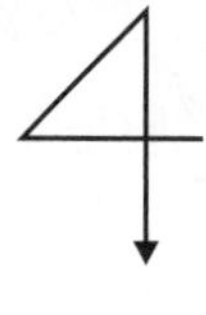
c

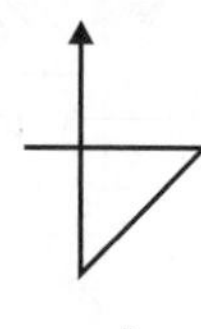
d

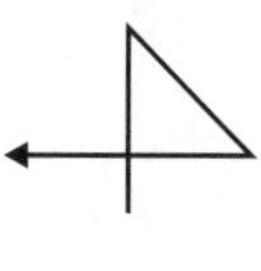
e

(5)

a b c d e

(6)

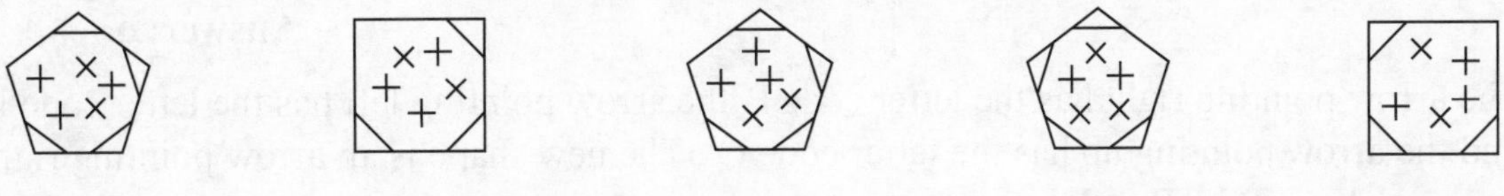

a b c d e

(7)

a b c d e

(8)

a b c d e

(9)

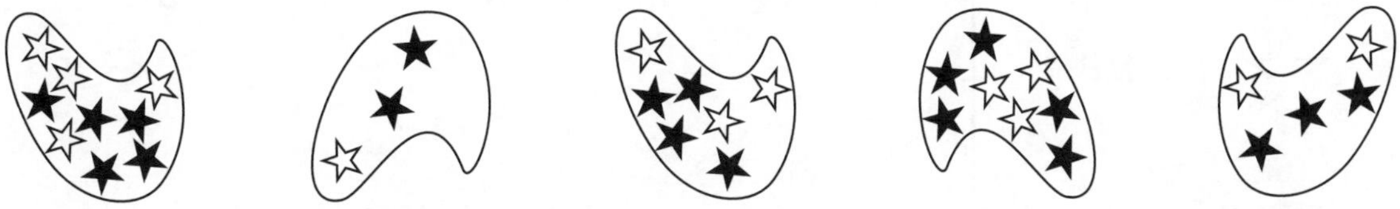

a b c d e

(10)

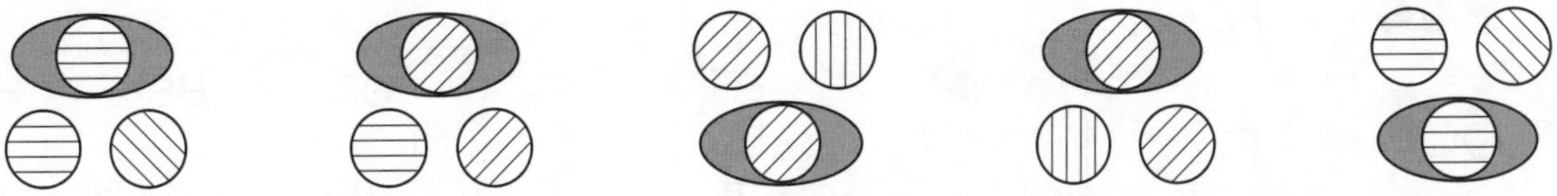

a b c d e

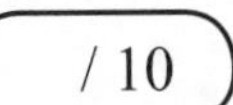
/ 10

Section 5 — Vertical Code

Each question has some shapes on the left with code letters that describe them. You need to work out what the code letters mean. There is then a shape on its own next to a choice of five codes. Work out which code describes this shape.

Example:

P

Q

R

P	Q	T	S	R
a	**b**	**c**	**d**	**e**

Answer: a

The arrow pointing right has the letter code P, the arrow pointing left has the letter code R, and the arrow pointing up has the letter code Q. The new shape is an arrow pointing right, so the code must be P and the answer is a.

Example:

BT

CS

BR

BC	CR	CT	BS	BR
a	**b**	**c**	**d**	**e**

Answer: d

Both black shapes have the letter code B, and the white shape has a C, so the first letter is the shading. The second letter code must be the code for shape. T stands for a pentagon, the letter S for a circle and the letter R for a triangle. The new shape must have a B because it is black, and an S because it is a circle. The code must be BS and the answer is d.

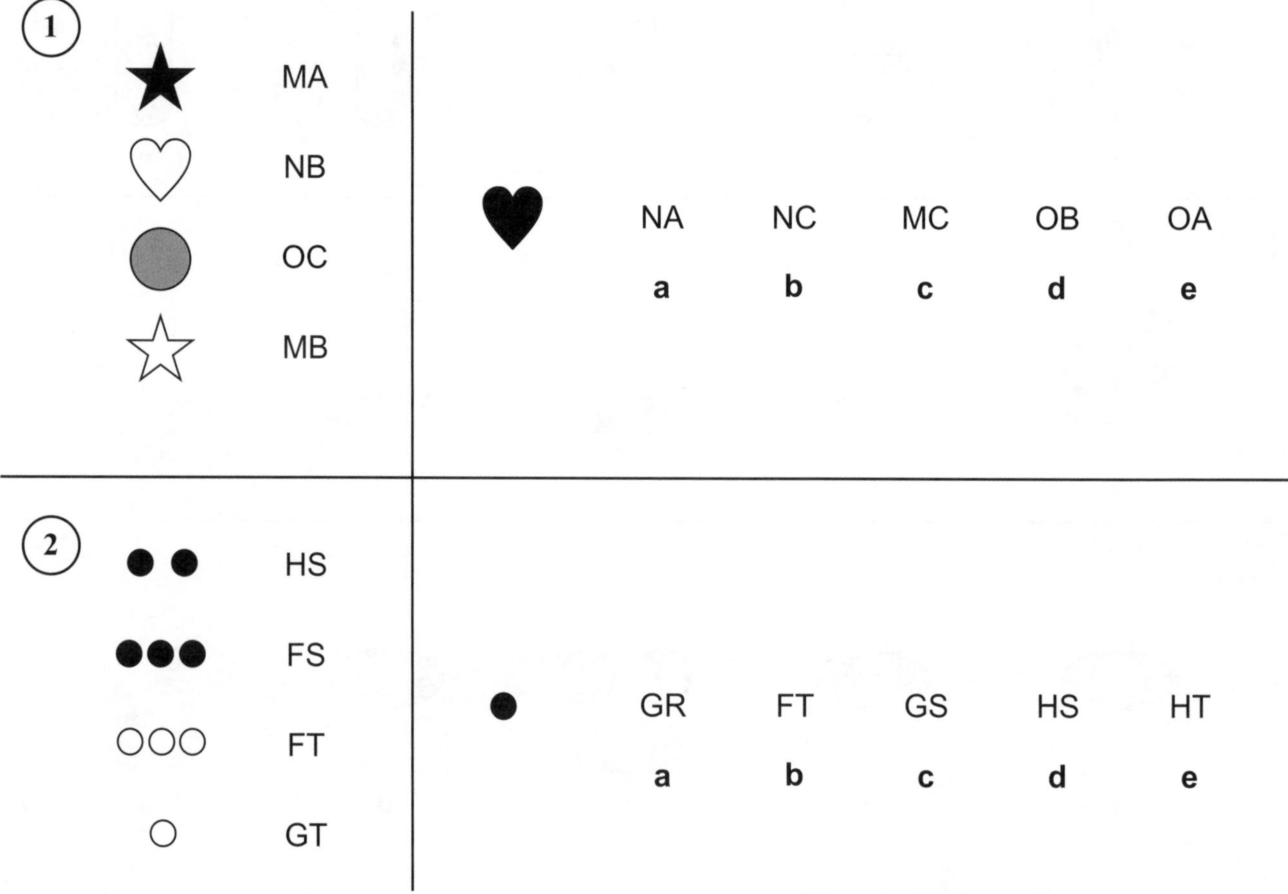

3

AV	
BV	AW **a** AV **b** BX **c** AB **d** BW **e**
BW	

4

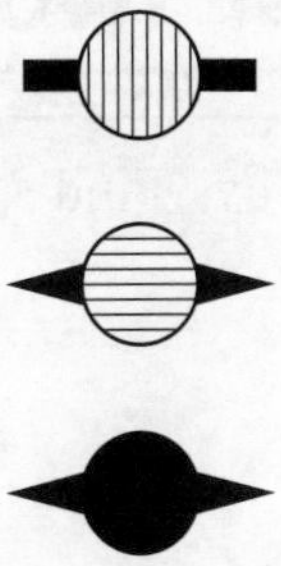

GL	
FN	FM **a** GN **b** GM **c** FL **d** FN **e**
FM	

5

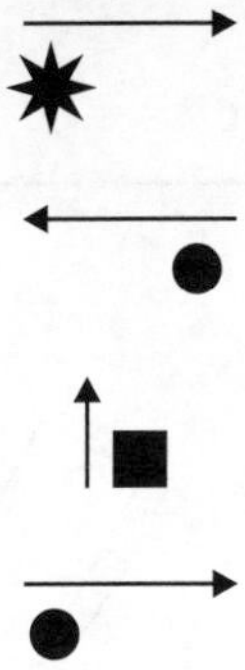

KP	
MQ	
LR	KR **a** LQ **b** MR **c** LP **d** MP **e**
KQ	

6

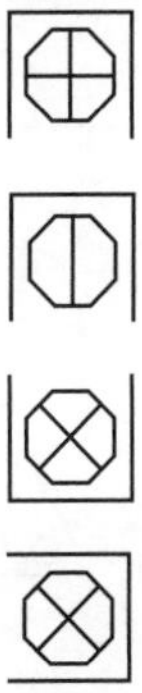

LC	
NC	
ME	LE **a** NC **b** LD **c** MC **d** ND **e**
MD	

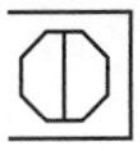

7

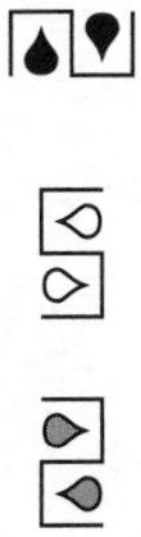

TL	
SN	TL **a** SM **b** TM **c** SL **d** SN **e**
TM	

8

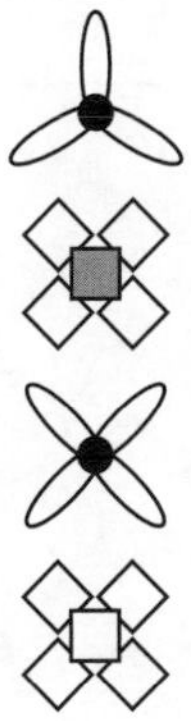

VPY	
WQZ	
VPZ	WQZ **a** VPQ **b** XPY **c** WPY **d** WQY **e**
XQZ	

/ 8 Total / 46

END OF TEST

Assessment Test 6

You can print **multiple-choice answer sheets** for these questions from our website — go to www.cgplearning.co.uk/11+. If you'd prefer to answer them in standard write-in format, just circle the letter underneath your answer. The test should take around 25 minutes.

Section 1 — Find the Figure Like the First Two

For each question below there are two figures that are like each other in some way. Find which of the five figures on the right is most like the two figures on the left.

Example:

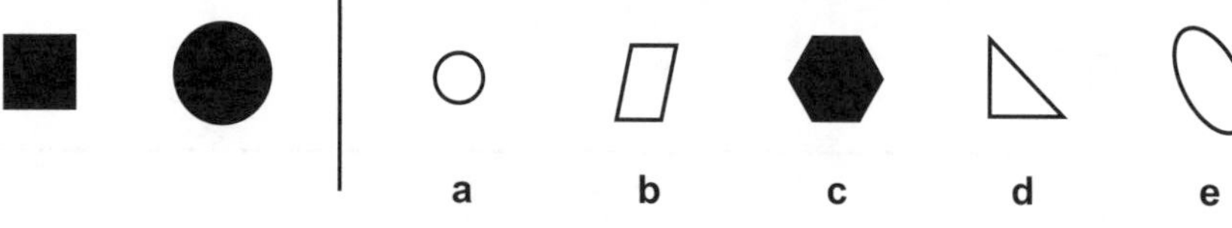

Answer: c

1

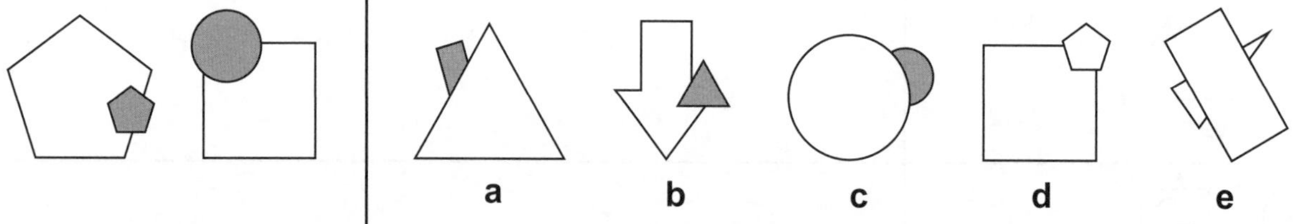

a b c d e

2

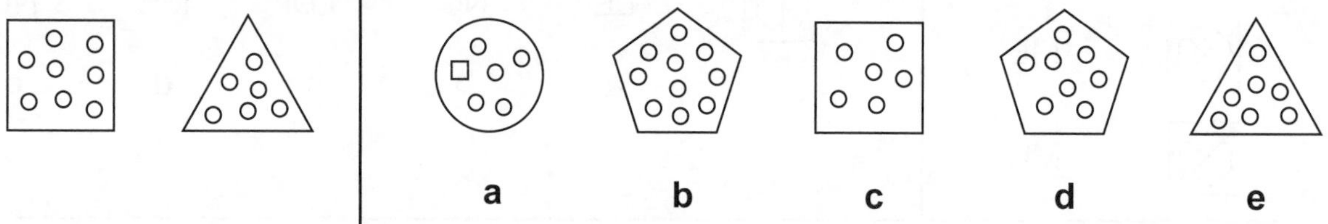

a b c d e

3

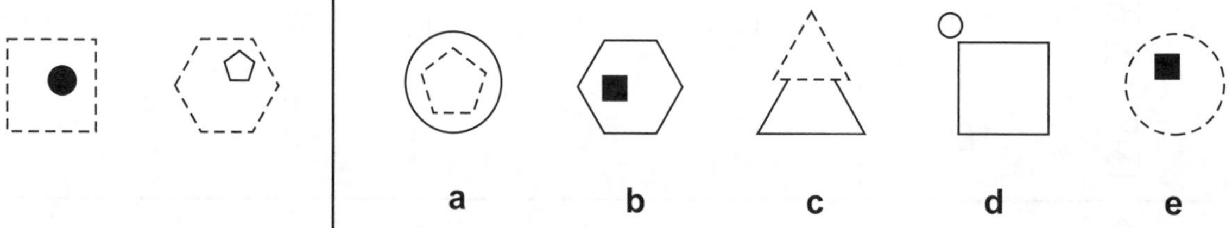

a b c d e

4

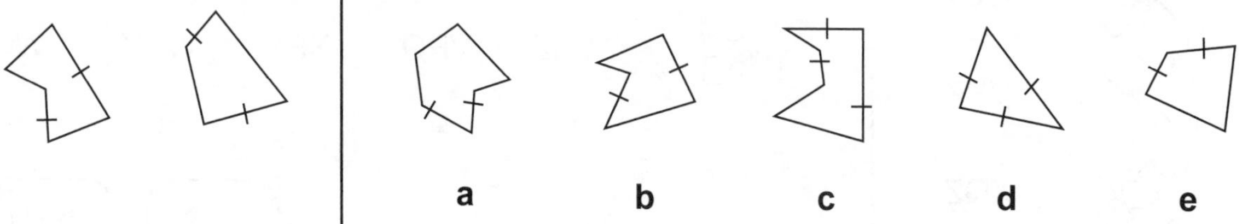

a b c d e

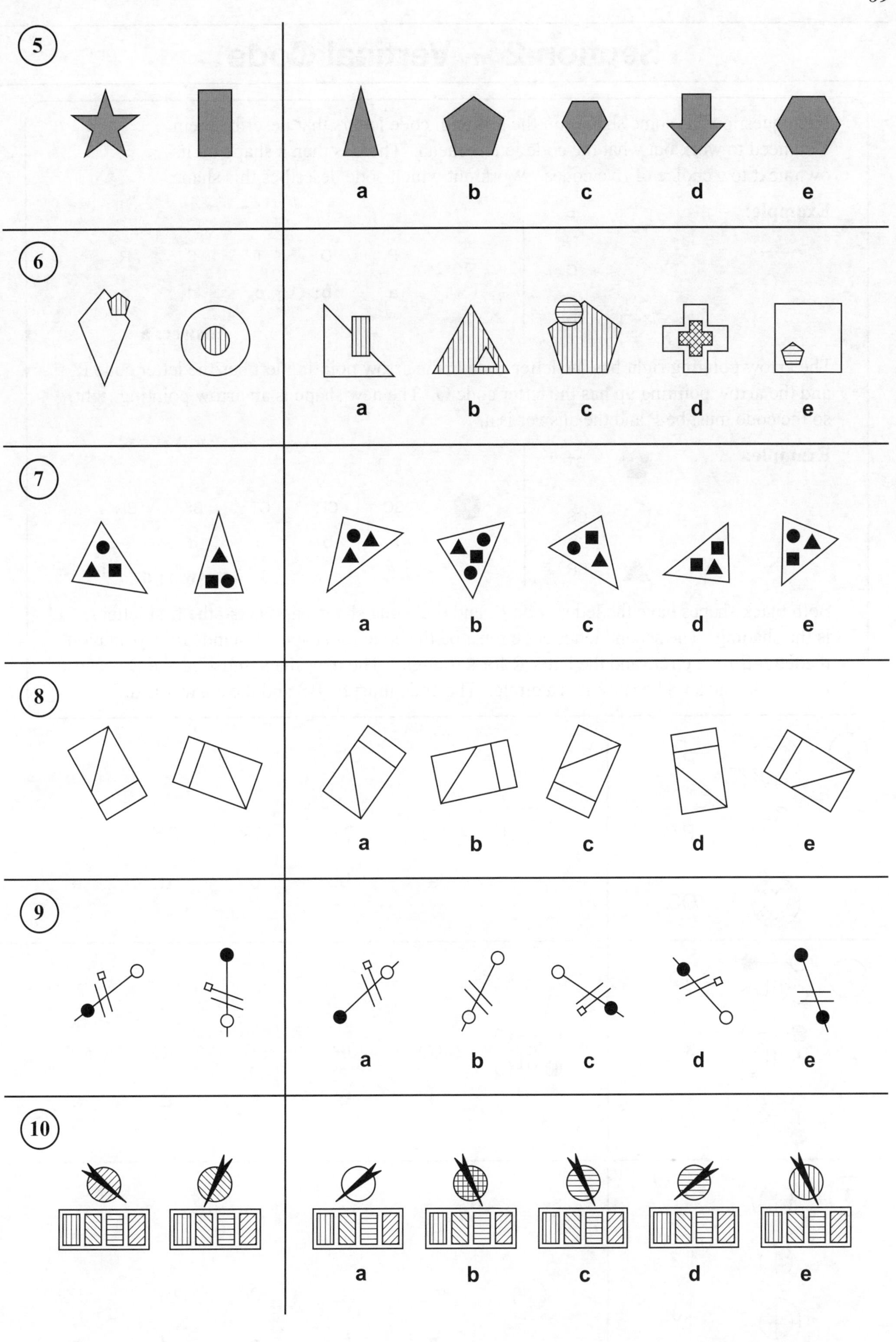

/ 10

Section 2 — Vertical Code

Each question has some shapes on the left with code letters that describe them. You need to work out what the code letters mean. There is then a shape on its own next to a choice of five codes. Work out which code describes this shape.

Example:

P

Q

R

P	Q	T	S	R
a	**b**	**c**	**d**	**e**

Answer: a

The arrow pointing right has the letter code P, the arrow pointing left has the letter code R, and the arrow pointing up has the letter code Q. The new shape is an arrow pointing right, so the code must be P and the answer is a.

Example:

BT

CS

BR

BC	CR	CT	BS	BR
a	**b**	**c**	**d**	**e**

Answer: d

Both black shapes have the letter code B, and the white shape has a C, so the first letter is the shading. The second letter code must be the code for shape. T stands for a pentagon, the letter S for a circle and the letter R for a triangle. The new shape must have a B because it is black, and an S because it is a circle. The code must be BS and the answer is d.

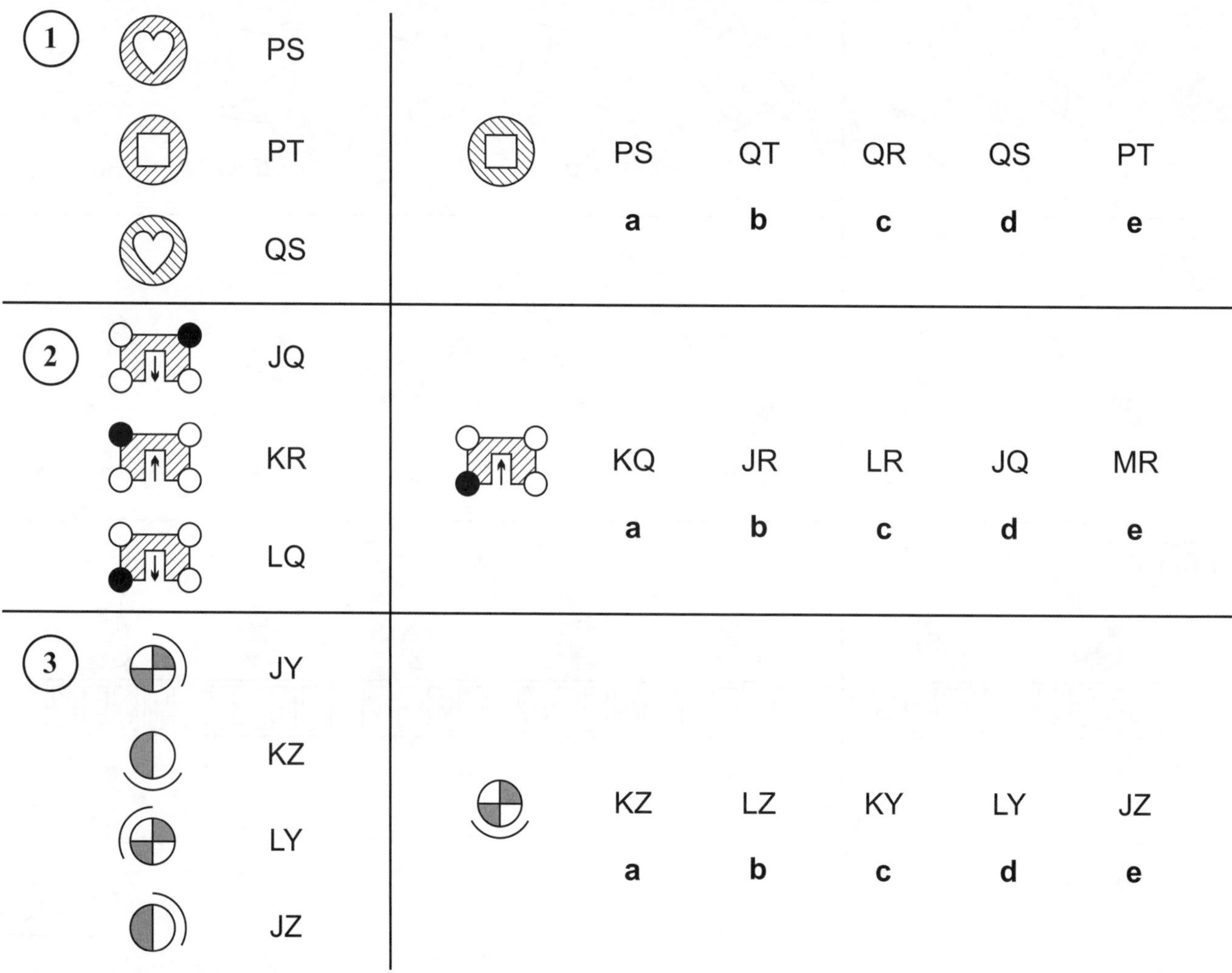

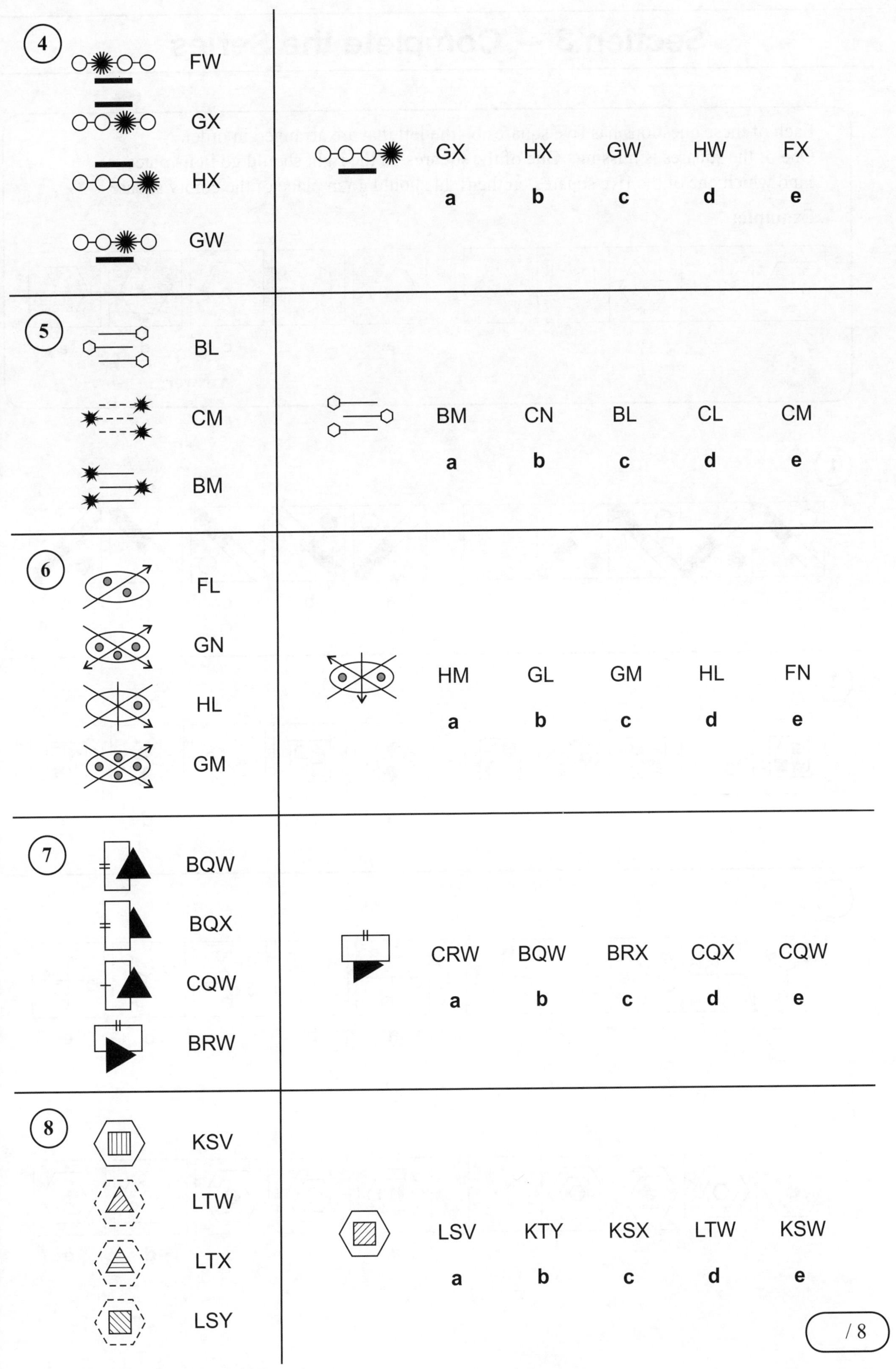
4
FW
GX
HX
GW
GX HX GW HW FX
a b c d e
5
BL
CM
BM
BM CN BL CL CM
a b c d e
6
FL
GN
HL
GM
HM GL GM HL FN
a b c d e
7
BQW
BQX
CQW
BRW
CRW BQW BRX CQX CQW
a b c d e
8
KSV
LTW
LTX
LSY
LSV KTY KSX LTW KSW
a b c d e
/ 8

Section 3 — Complete the Series

Each of these questions has five squares on the left that are arranged in order.
One of the squares is missing. One of the squares on the right should go in its place.
Find which one of the five squares on the right should go in place of the empty square.

Example:

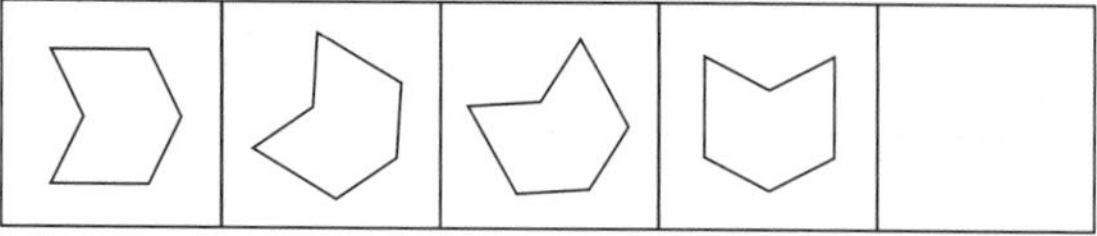
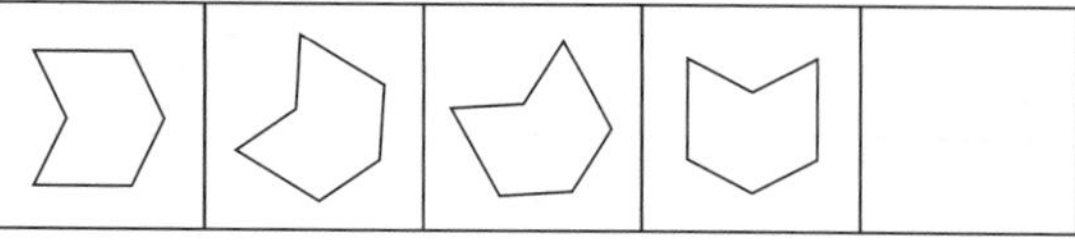
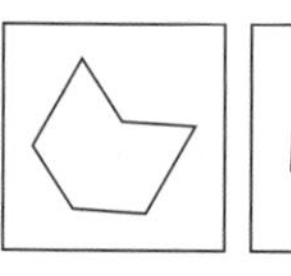
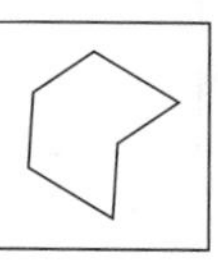
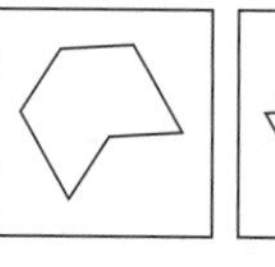
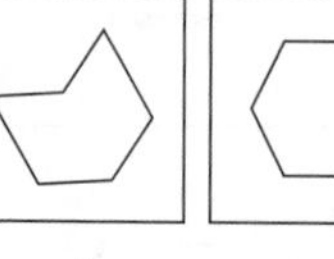

a b c d e

Answer: a

1

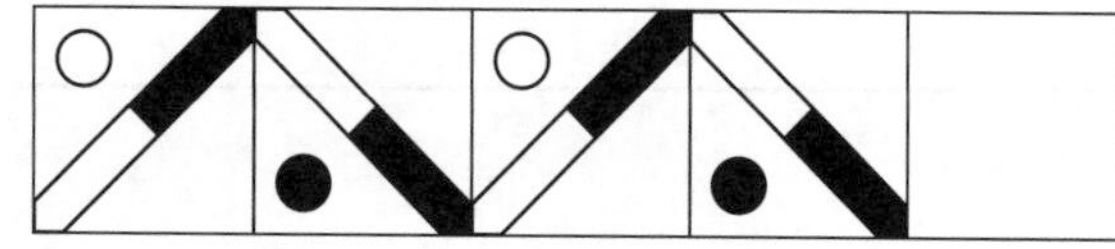
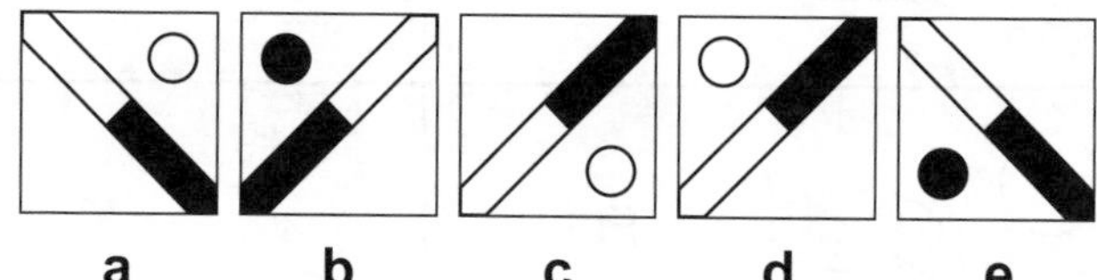

a b c d e

2

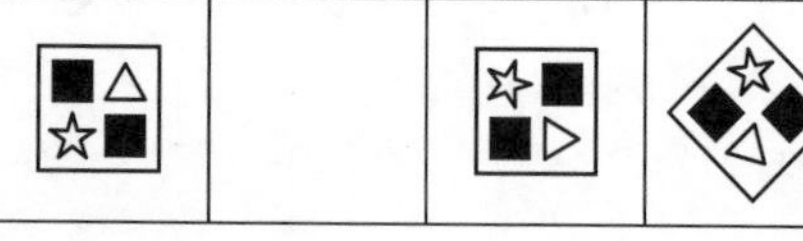

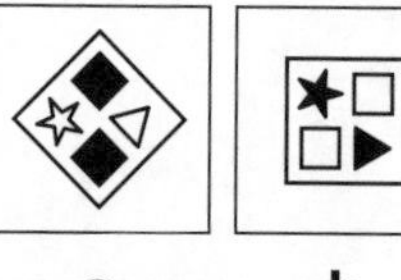
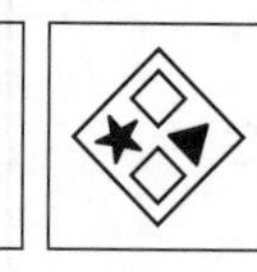
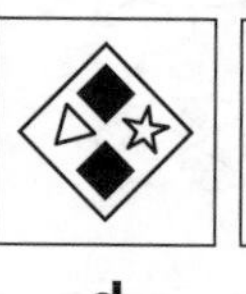

a b c d e

3

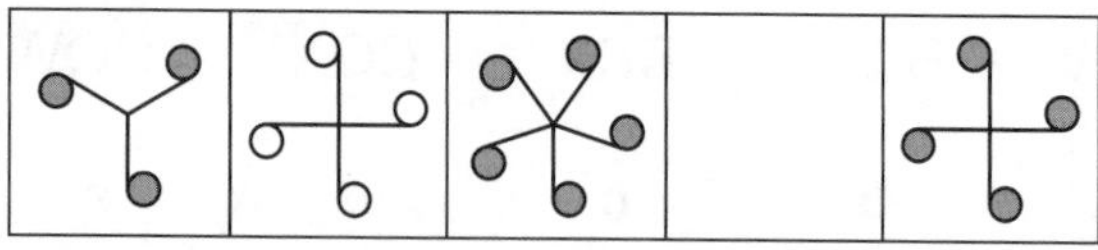
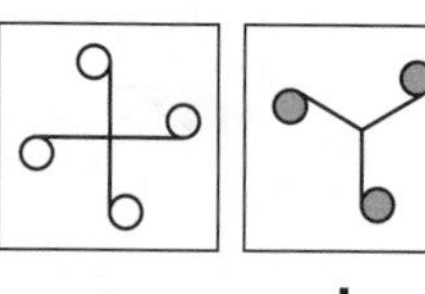
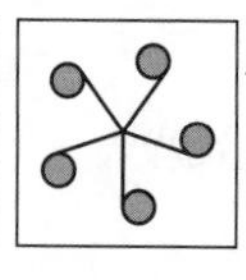
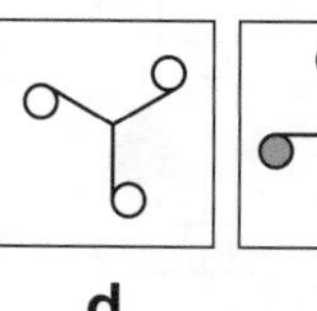
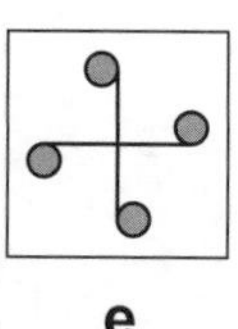

a b c d e

4

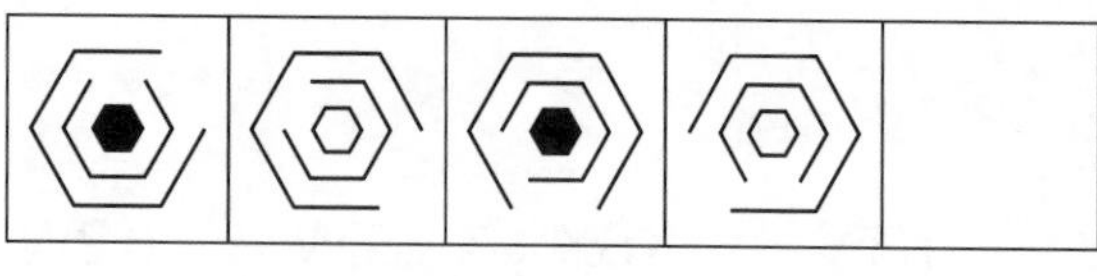
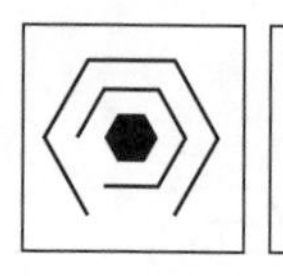
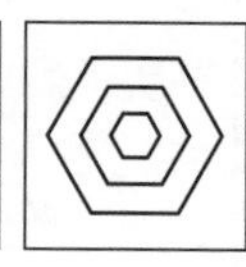
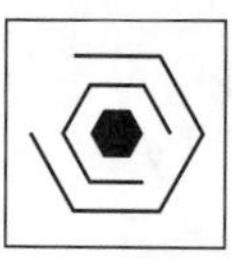
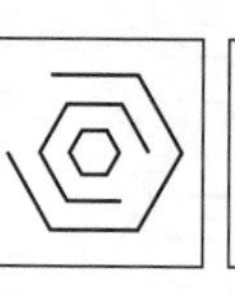
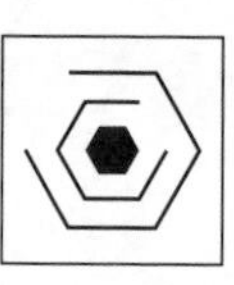

a b c d e

5

a b c d e

6

a b c d e

7

a b c d e

8

a b c d e

9

a b c d e

10

a b c d e

/ 10

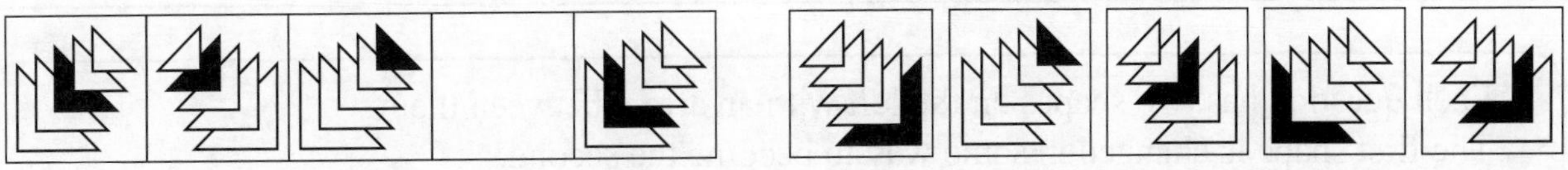

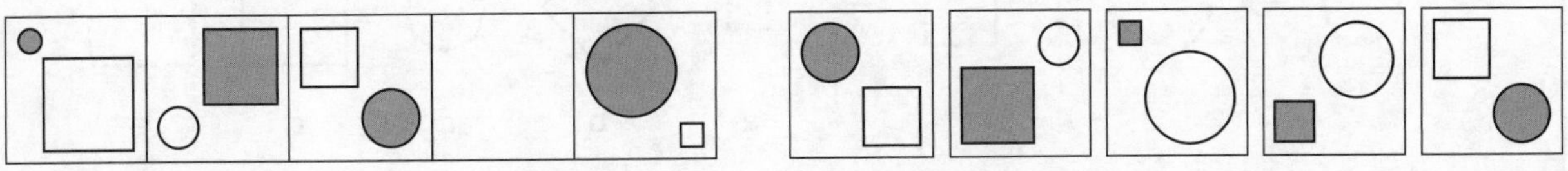

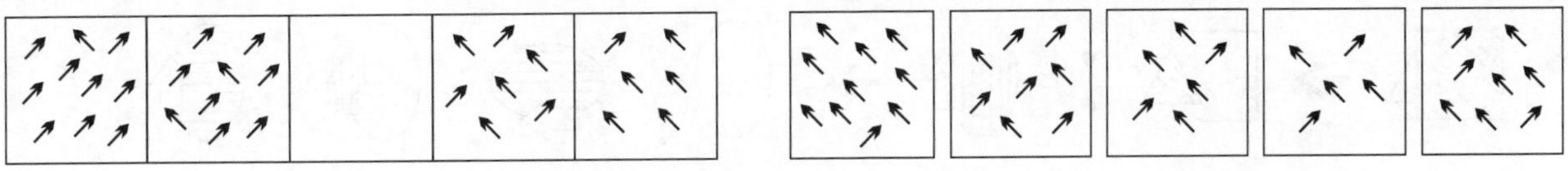

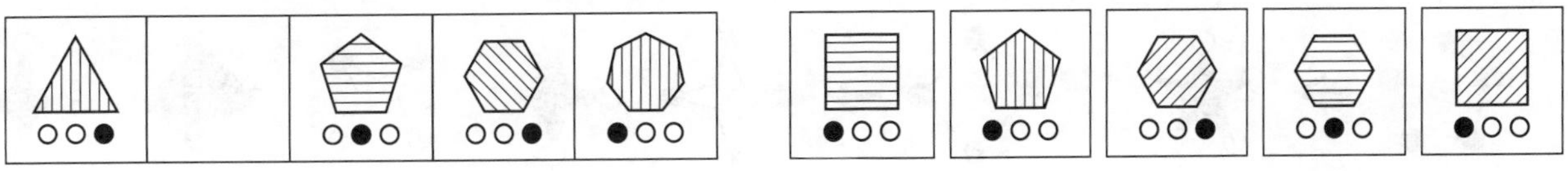

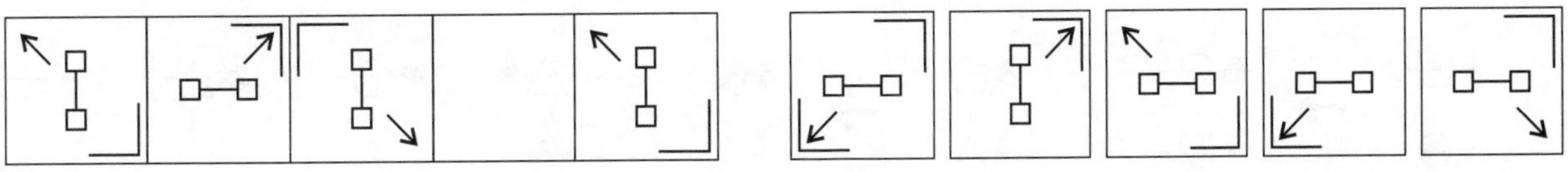

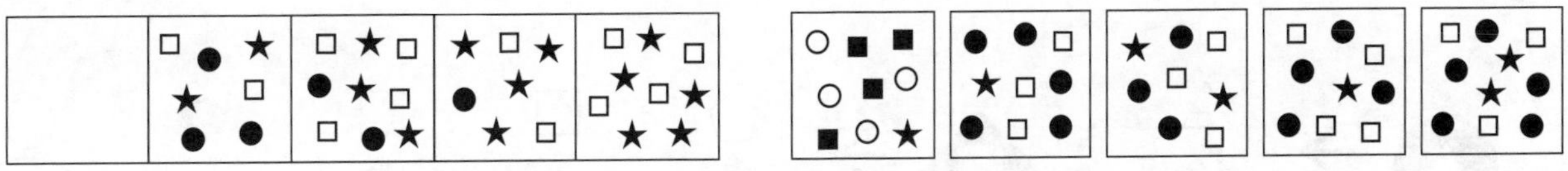

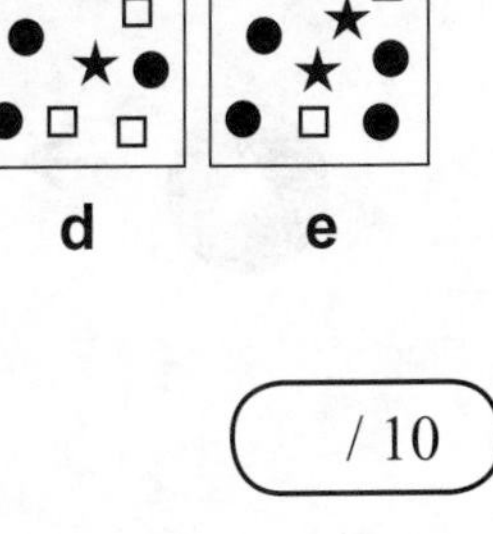

Section 4 — Complete the Pair

Each question has two shapes on the left with an arrow between them.
The first shape is changed in some way to become the second.
There is then a third shape followed by an arrow and a choice of five shapes.
Choose the shape on the right that relates to the third shape like the second does to the first.

Example:

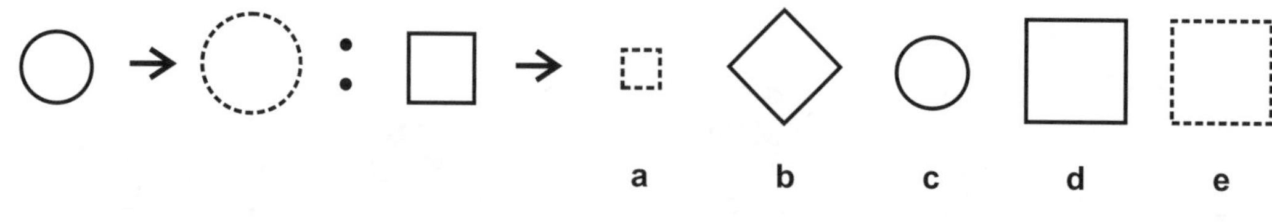

Answer: e

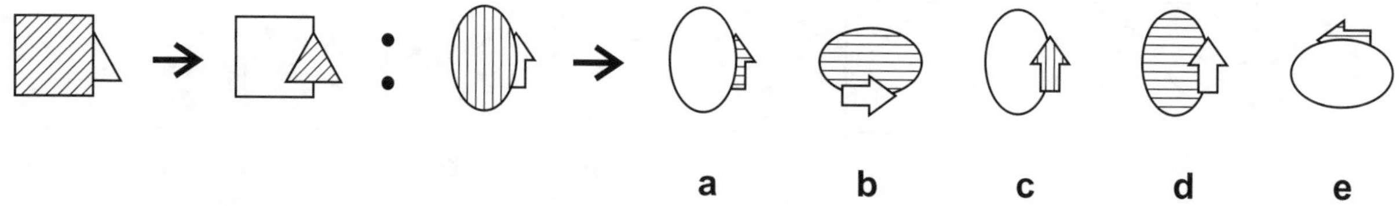

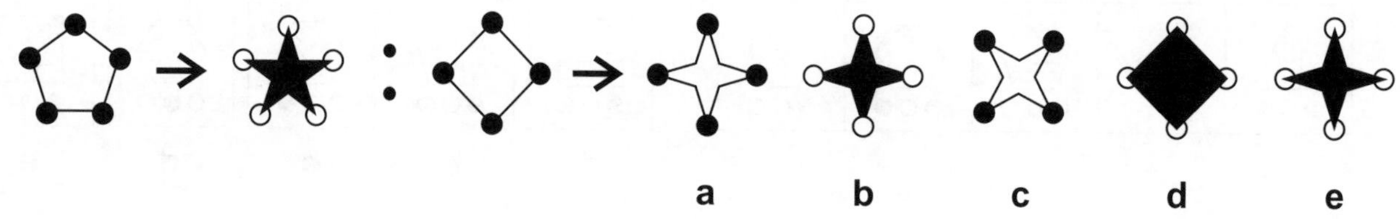

3

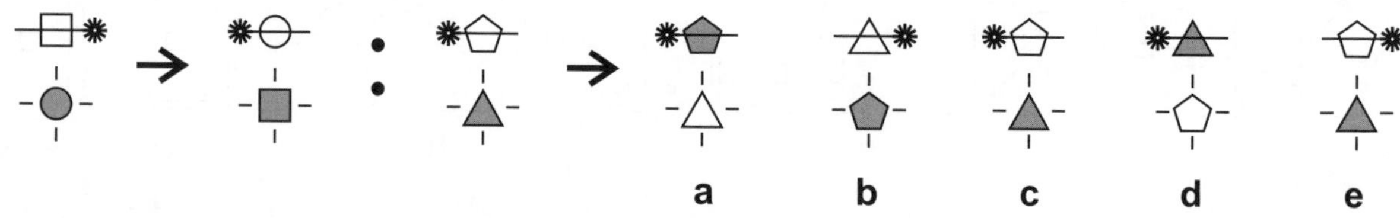

4

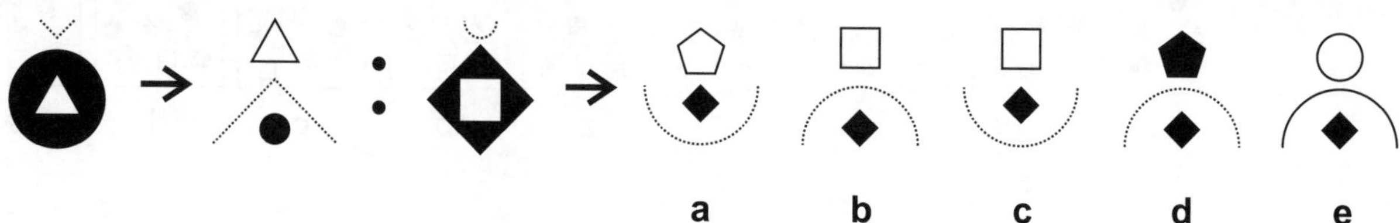

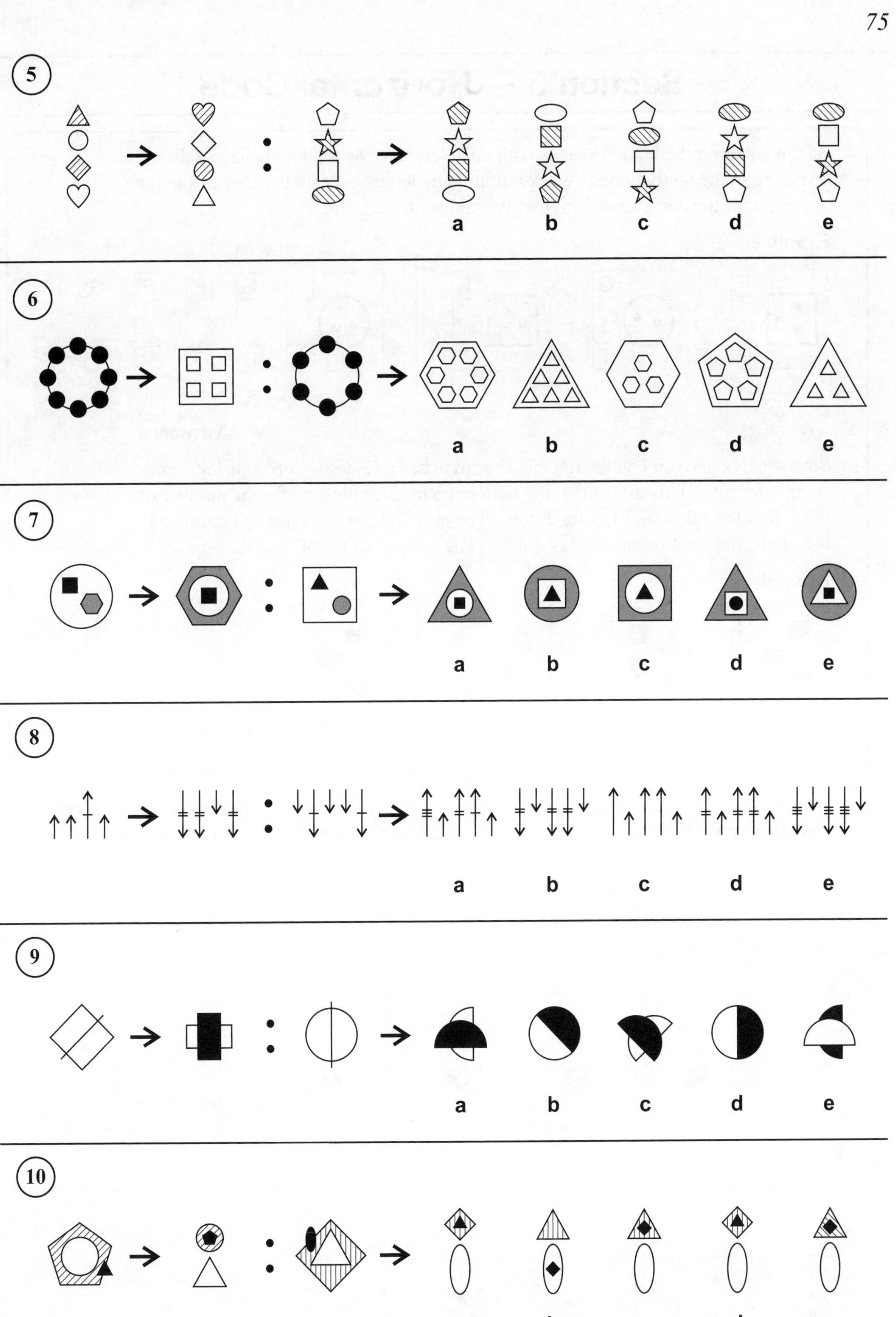

/ 10

Section 5 — Horizontal Code

In the boxes on the left are shapes with code letters. The top letters have a different meaning to the bottom ones. Work out how the letters go with the shapes and then find the code for the new shape from the five codes on the right.

Example:

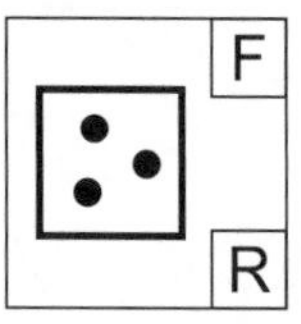
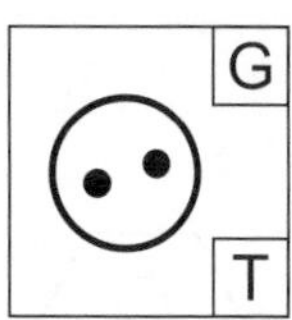
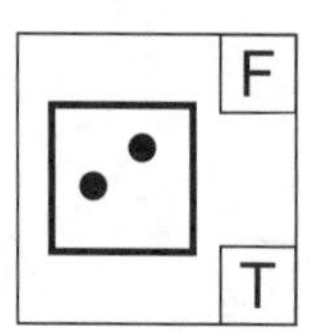
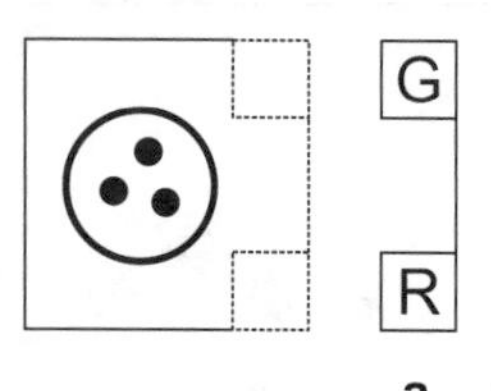
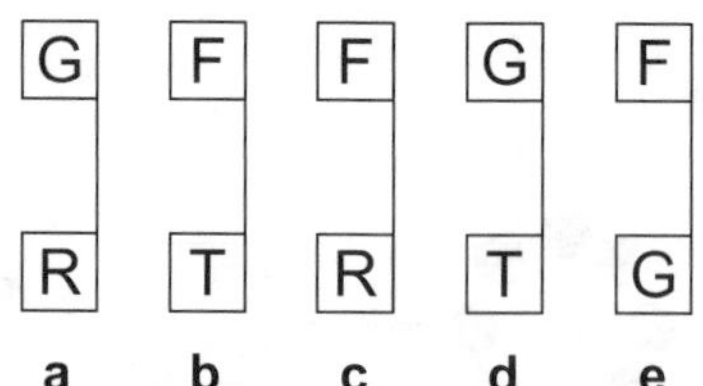

Answer: a

Both squares have an F at the top, but the circle has a G, so the top code letter must stand for shape. This means that the bottom code letter must be for the number of dots. R is for 3 dots and T is for 2 dots. The new figure must have a G because it is a circle and an R because it has 3 dots. The code must be GR and the answer is a.

Example:

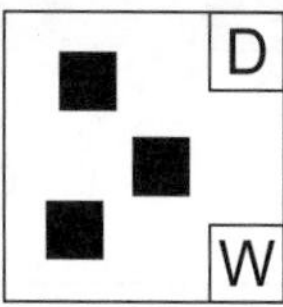
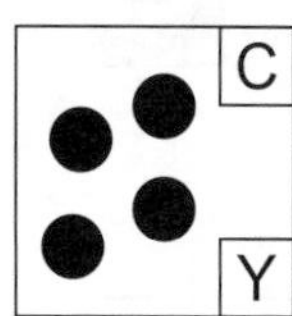
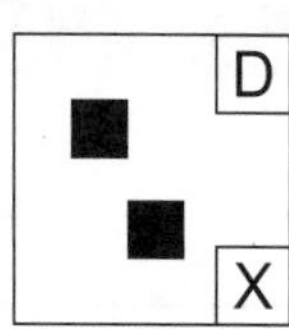
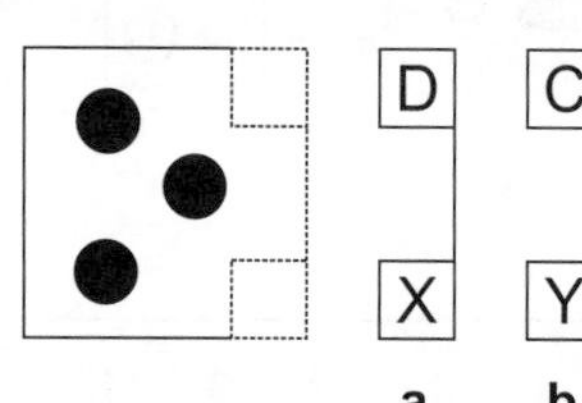
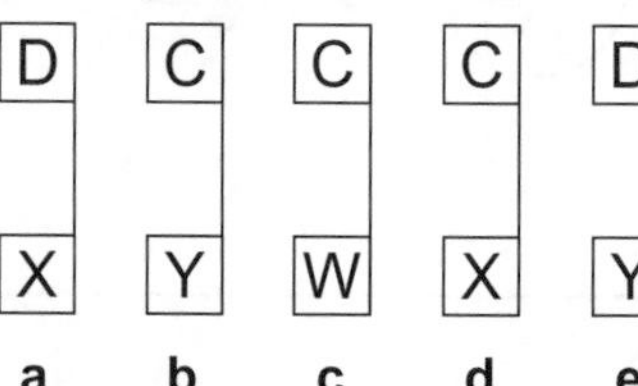

Answer: c

Both figures with squares have a D at the top, and the figure with circles has a C, so the top code letter must be for shape. The bottom code letter must be for the number of shapes. W is for 3 shapes, Y is for 4 and X is for 2. The new figure must have a C because it is made of circles and a W because there are 3 of them. The code must be CW and the answer is c.

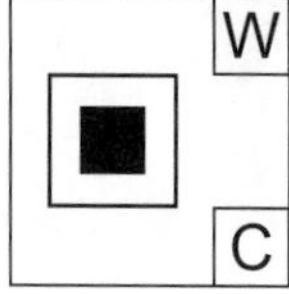
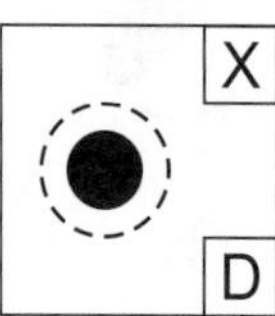
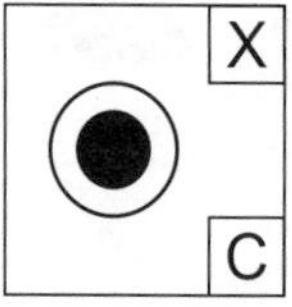
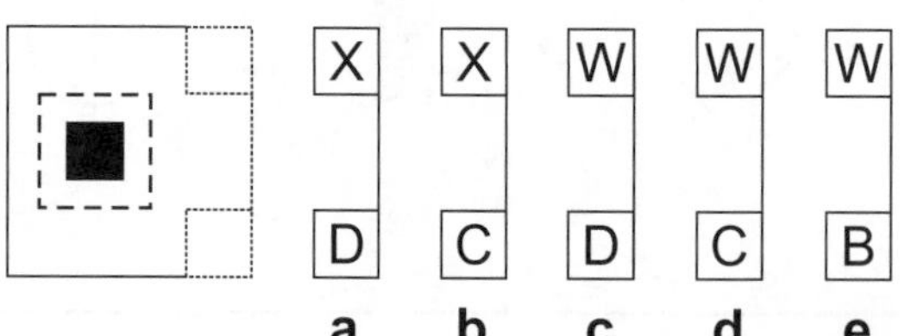

2

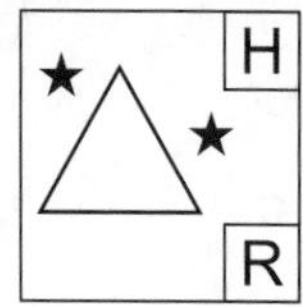
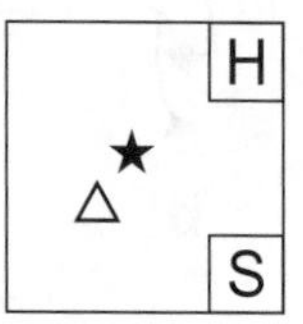
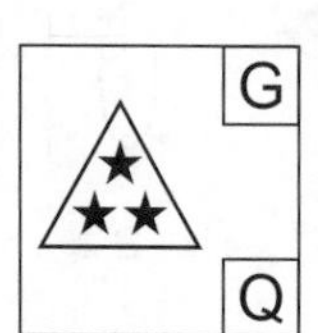
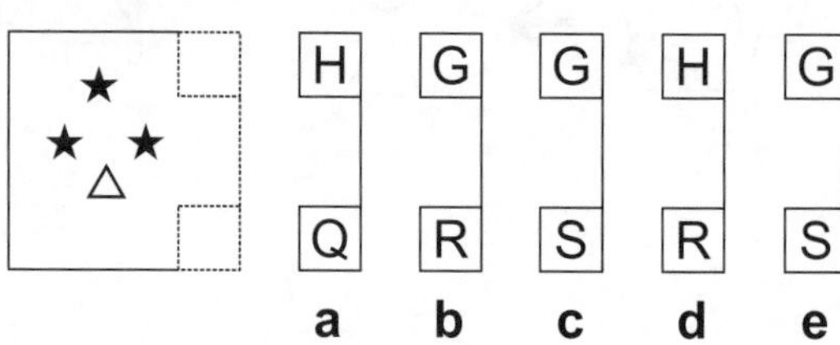

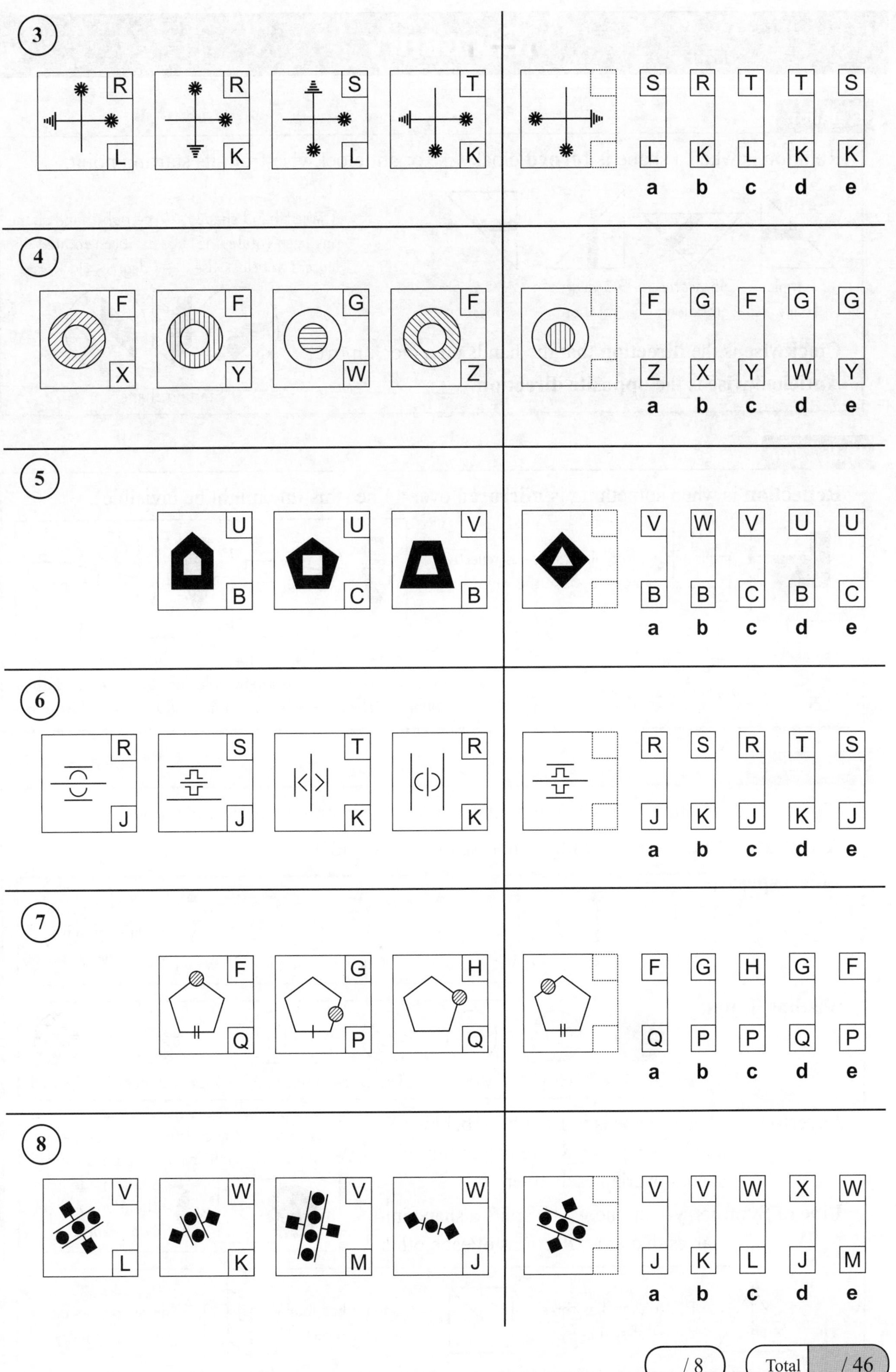

/ 8 Total / 46

END OF TEST

Glossary

Rotation

Rotation is when a shape is **turned** clockwise or anticlockwise from its starting point.

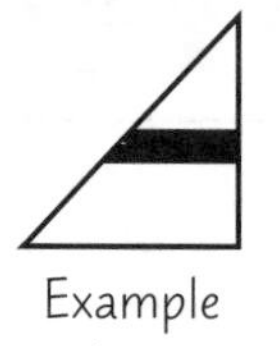

Example shape

45 degree rotation

90 degree rotation

180 degree rotation

The left hand shape has been rotated 45 degrees anticlockwise.

The right hand shape has been rotated 45 degrees clockwise.

Starting shape

Clockwise is the **direction** that the hands on a clock move.
Anticlockwise is the **opposite direction**.

Reflection

Reflection is when something is **mirrored** over a line (this line might be invisible).

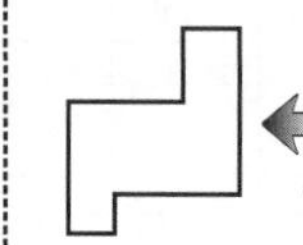

The black shape is reflected across to make the white shape.

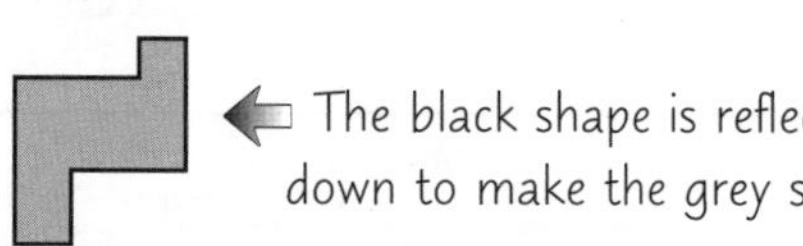

The black shape is reflected down to make the grey shape.

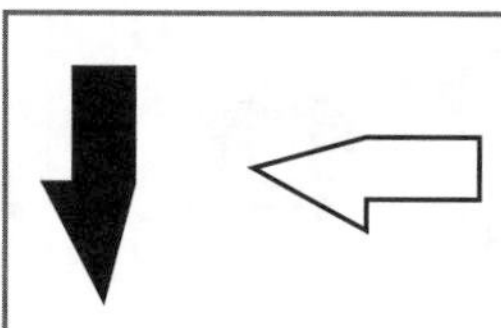

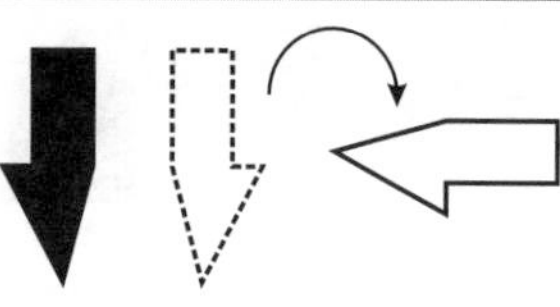

To get from the black shape to the white shape, first you need to reflect it across an invisible line (to make the dashed shape). Then you need to rotate it 90 degrees clockwise.

Other terms

Figure — the picture as a whole that makes up one example or option in a question.

Arrow-style Line — a line with a small shape at one end.

Line Types:

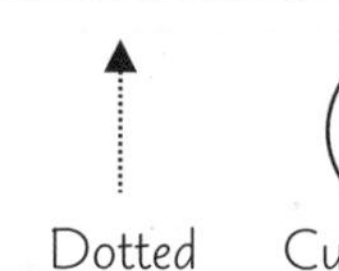

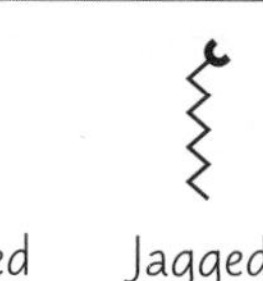

Thin, Thick, Dashed, Dotted, Curved, Jagged, Wavy

Arrow-style lines of different line types.

Shading Types:

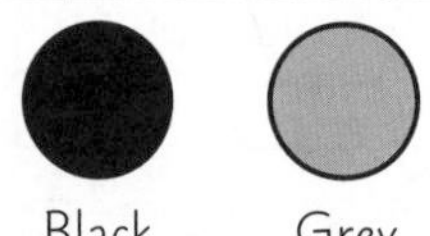

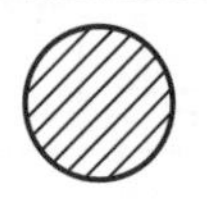

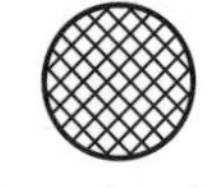

Black, Grey, White, Two types of hatching, Cross-hatched, Spotted

Layering — when a shape is in front of or behind another shape, or where two or more shapes overlap each other.

Layering — the circle is in front of the square. The right hand shape is a cut-out shape made from the overlap of the two shapes.

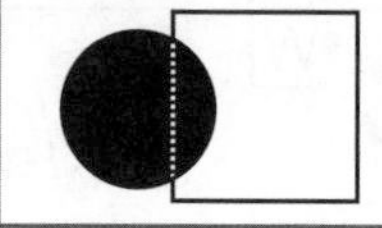

Line of Symmetry — a line which splits a shape into halves that are reflections of each other.

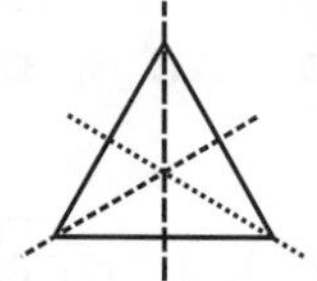

This triangle has three lines of symmetry.

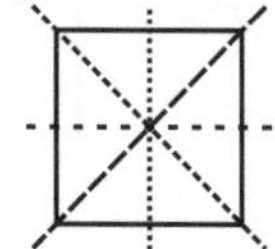

A square has four lines of symmetry.

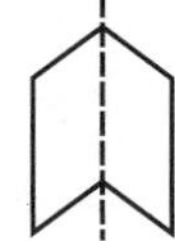

This shape has one line of symmetry.